D0241742

YOU DO THAT AND I'LL SLING YOU IN JAIL!
SALOO
£6.20

WHEN little Eric eats a banana, he turns into the Dandy's super hero —
KAPOW!
BANANAMAN
One day, at Police Headquarters —
CRIME HAS GONE DOWN SO I'VE GOT SOMETHING TO GIVE YOU, 'NANA KNICKERS.
CRIME WAVE FIGURES
WHAT'S THAT, CHIEF O'REILLY? A GOLDEN HANDSHAKE.

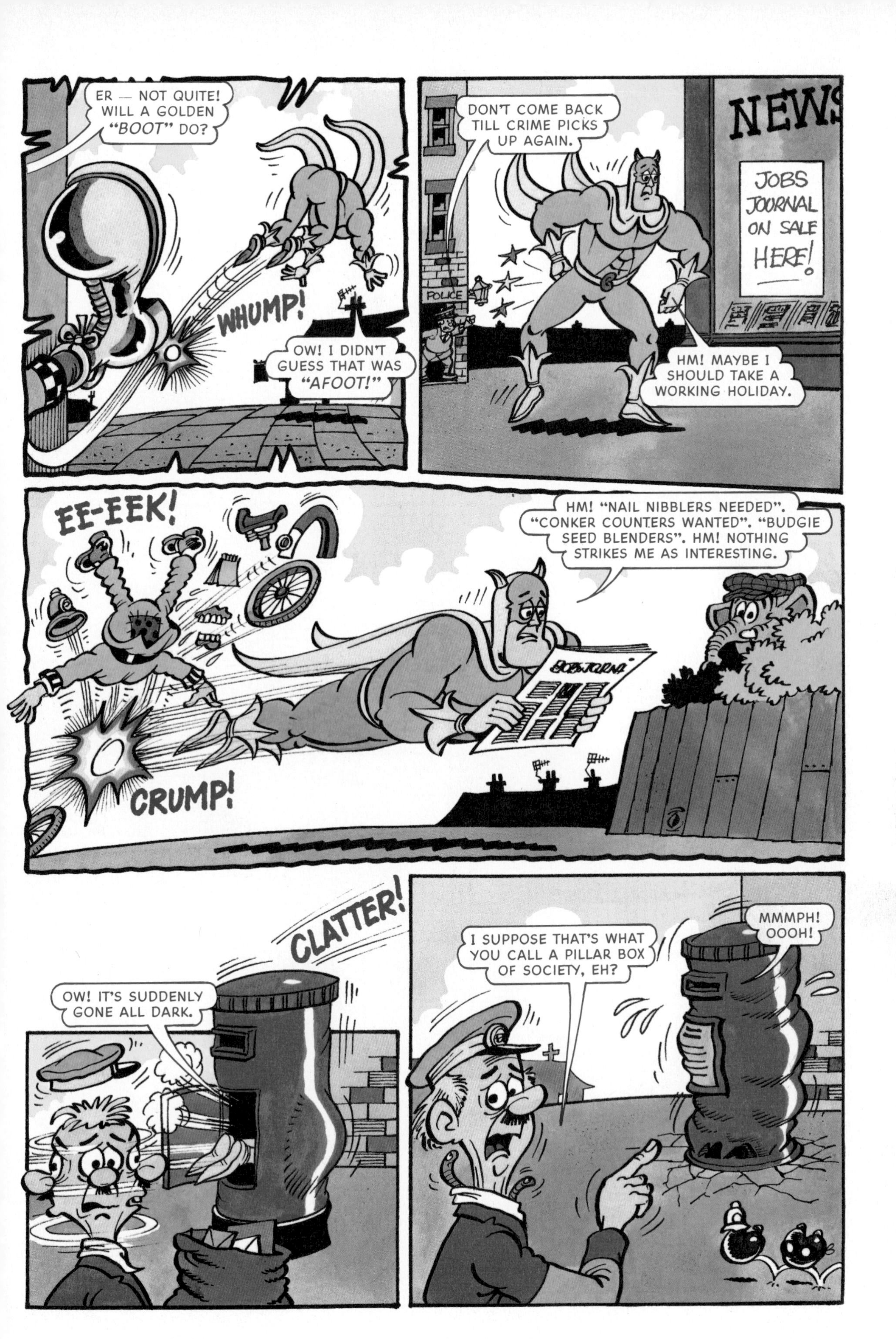
ER — NOT QUITE! WILL A GOLDEN "BOOT" DO?
WHUMP!
OW! I DIDN'T GUESS THAT WAS "AFOOT!"
DON'T COME BACK TILL CRIME PICKS UP AGAIN.
NEWS
JOBS JOURNAL ON SALE HERE!
POLICE
HM! MAYBE I SHOULD TAKE A WORKING HOLIDAY.
EE-EEK!
HM! "NAIL NIBBLERS NEEDED". "CONKER COUNTERS WANTED". "BUDGIE SEED BLENDERS". HM! NOTHING STRIKES ME AS INTERESTING.
CRUMP!
CLATTER!
OW! IT'S SUDDENLY GONE ALL DARK.
I SUPPOSE THAT'S WHAT YOU CALL A PILLAR BOX OF SOCIETY, EH?
MMMPH! OOOH!

AH! I'M FREE! WELL, ALMOST!

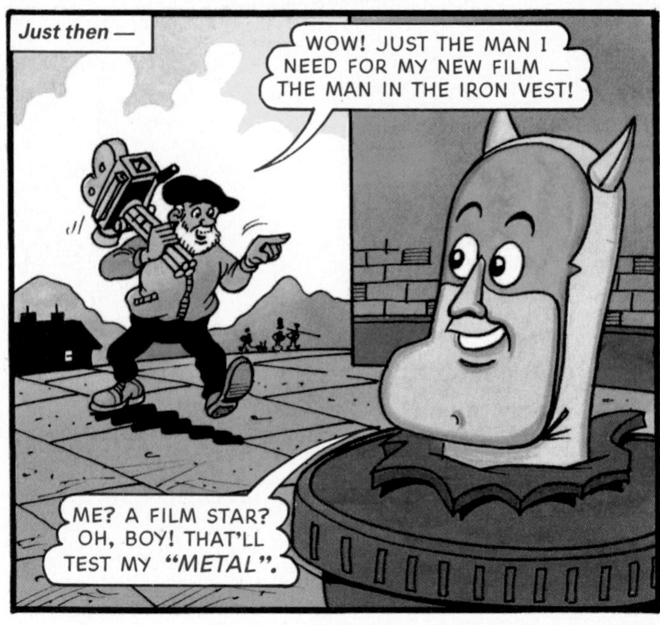
Just then —
WOW! JUST THE MAN I NEED FOR MY NEW FILM — THE MAN IN THE IRON VEST!
ME? A FILM STAR? OH, BOY! THAT'LL TEST MY "METAL".

Later, on the film set —
YOU ARE A TYRANT — AND THE KING'S ENEMY.
HM! SOUNDS A BIT TAME.

Suddenly —
TAKE THAT, YOU TIN TRAITOR.
OOF! WHAT A DIRTY KNIGHT.
ZUMP!

OOH! AAH! I'VE BEEN "RUMBLED". NOW I'M GOING FOR A SPIN IN THE COUNTRYSIDE.
RUMBLE!
RUMBLE!
RUMBLE!

EEK! I'M REALLY MAKING A "SPLASH" IN THIS FILM.
WHUMP!
SPOSH!
THAT WASN'T MEANT TO HAPPEN! RESCUE SQUAD!

THANK GOODNESS FOR MAGNETS, EH, BLUE BONCE?
ER — THEY DO HAVE THEIR "ATTRACTIONS".
Suddenly, out of the blue —
AAIIEEE! I'VE "SINGED" MY CONTRACT.
OOH! EVERYTHING HAPPENS LIKE LIGHTNING ON A FILM SET.
Later —
HM! BANANAMAN SEEMS TO BE HAVING ALL THE LUCK.
DEER CHIEFY, LYING AROUND DOING NUFFIN GOOD TAN! BANANAMAN X
CHIEFY THE COP SHOP BANANATOWN
But —
I'M NOT REALLY! I'M JUST A "BURNT-OUT" FILM STAR.

MOLLY

HMMM!
HUH?

PATHETIC!
SQUEAL!

NO FLIPPIN' WONDER WITH YOU AS A DAUGHTER.
HUP!
THAT GIRL NEXT DOOR HAS A TOUGH, BUTCH DAD AND MINE IS A GIBBERING TWIT OF A SAP.

IT'S TIME YOU TOUGHENED UP.
ANYTHING YOU SAY, PRECIOUS PICKLE-HEART SWEETUMS.

AT LEAST WE'LL TOUGHEN YOU UP IF YOU CAN GET THE LID OF THE BLOOMIN' BOX.
PUFF!

ALLO, WIMPY NEIGHBOUR.
PING
TIME FOR SOME DESPERATE MEASURES . . .

. . . STARTING WITH THIS.
COW-PIE
I'LL NEVER EAT ALL·THAT.

OH YES YOU WILL, MATEY.
GRAAAH!

WOOH! I'VE GOT MUSCLES.
NOT BAD, BUT IT NEEDS MORE.

AND THIS IS JUST THE STUFF.
HAIR RESTORER

TA-DA! FINISHED.
RRRR!
GOOD EH?
MEET MY ALL-NEW, SUPER-IMPROVED *DESPERATE DAD.*

SOON GET RID OF HIM . . .
PING
A CHIN LIKE STEEL, MATE.

. . . MMM!
THROB

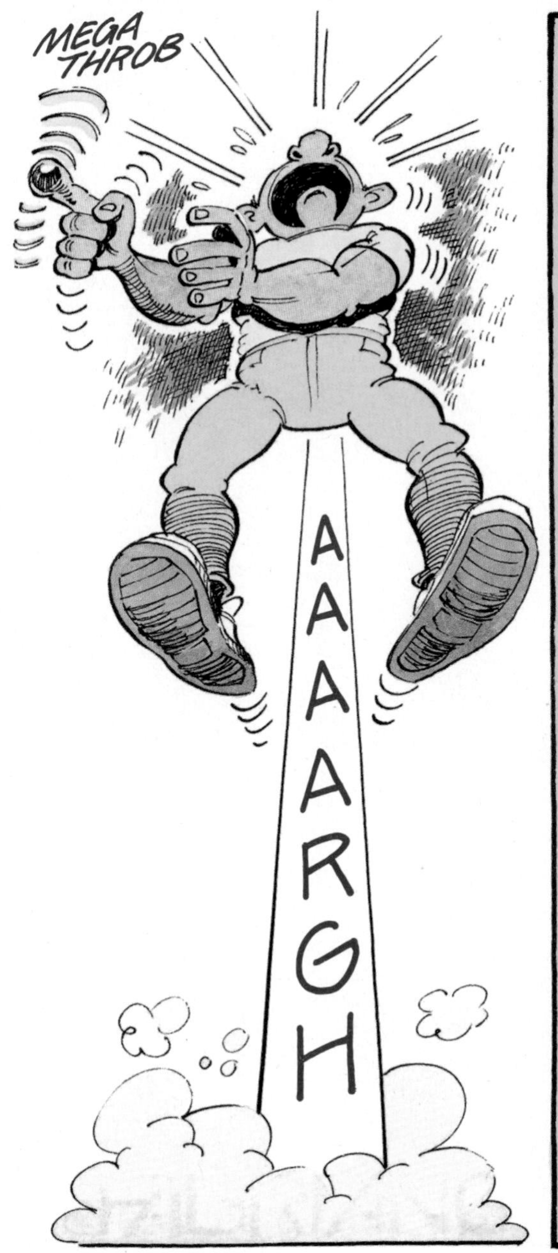
MEGA THROB
AAAARGH

THIS IS MUCH MORE LIKE IT.
PUFF!
WAIL!

THAT'S MY DAD — I'M ALMOST PROUD OF HIM.
SUCH PRAISE.

OOH! SHARP STUBBLE.
JAB

WAAAGH! VERY SHARP STUBBLE!
OH, NO.
I MIGHT BE THE TOUGHEST DAD ABOUT BUT MOLLY'S WAY TOO TOUGH FOR ME. OOH, CRUMBS.
WALLY! THAT HURT, YOU STEAMIN' NIT!
NUTS

BLINKY'S REALLY HARD PUZZLE

CREATURE FEATURES

DESPERATE DAN
HOWDY, Y'ALL!
ONE DAY IN CACTUSVILLE —
WHAT'S THIS?
CACTUSVILLE SUN
WATER FOUND ON MOON!
THEN —
READ ALL ABOUT IT! WATER FOUND ON THE MOON!
CACTUSVILLE SUN
WATER FOUND ON MOON!
HUH! THAT AIN'T NEWS.

SIT YOURSELF DOWN AN' I'LL TELL YOU WHAT HAPPENED LAST YEAR.
GO ON, OLD-TIMER. I DO LIKE TO HEAR A GOOD FAIRY TALE.
IT WAS THE HEIGHT OF SUMMER AND CACTUSVILLE WAS FEELIN' THE HEAT.

EVERYTHING'S DYING THROUGH LACK OF WATER, DAN.
IT SURE IS, MR MAYOR.

SUDDENLY —
HEY! I'VE JUST BEEN STRUCK BY AN IDEA.

AND SO —
AIN'T THIS A DIVINE IDEA? I'LL TRY TO FIND WATER WITH THIS TWIG.

HUH? IT'S POINTING UPWARDS.
BECAUSE THERE IS WATER ON THE MOON.

I, PROFESSOR NUTTS KNOW THIS. AND I WANT YOU TO GO TO THE MOON AND PROVE IT.
THAT SOUNDS LIKE DESPERATE FUN, PROF.

GOODBYE. HAVE A NICE TRIP.
CHEERIO! I'LL BE BACK IN TWO SHAKES OF A SPACESHIP.

SO —
LANDED — AND AIN'T THAT LUCKY? RIGHT BESIDE A POND!

JUST AS WELL I BROUGHT A LONG HOSE WITH ME.

HM! I SEEM TO HAVE LOST MY HAT BUT I CAN'T BE BOTHERED LOOKING FOR IT.

I'D BETTER GET BACK TO EARTH AND TELL FOLKS THE GOOD NEWS.

AT LAST —
CACTUSVILLE, HERE I COME. PITY ABOUT MY HAT, THOUGH.

DAN LANDS IN ONE PIECE — ALMOST!
WELL DONE, DAN. OUR LAKES AND PONDS WILL SOON BE FILLED WITH MOON WATER.

YOU DESERVE SOMETHING FOR YOUR EFFORTS. HAVE A SWEET.
GEE! THANKS!

BACK AT THE NEWSPAPER OFFICE —
HAW-HAW-HAW! THAT'S THE DAFTEST STORY I'VE EVER HEARD IN MY WHOLE LIFE.
DARN IT! IT'S THE TRUTH, I TELL YOU.

THERE! AIN'T THAT PROOF?
ARE YOU TELLING THE TRUTH OR ARE YOU JUST TRYING TO PULL DAN'S HAT OVER MY EYES?
LATEST.
ASTRONAUTS FIND HAT ON MOON.
WHAT D'YOU THINK, READERS?

Cat Tips
A guide to living for today's cat

ROWFF! ROWFF! BOW-WOW-WOW!
DOGS LOVE CHASING US CATS.

BUT THEY CAN'T CLIMB TREES, SO WE ESCAPE.

UH? A SLIPPERY TREE?

AW, NUTS.
CACKLE!
OIL

CACKLE! HAR-HAR!
MEOWL!

Later —
YEP! THAT DOPEY MUTT IS AFTER ME AGAIN.
WOOF!

BUT THIS TIME I HAVE A CUNNING PLAN.
UH?
LEAP
ZOOM

WOOFYAH!
WAP
HIS PAWS DON'T HAVE BRAKES.

AND WHAT DO YOU KNOW? THE HOUND IS GOOD FOR CLIMBING TREES — AS A LADDER.
GROAN!

BERYL the PERIL
SHIFT, PARENT! COMING THROUGH! IT'S NOSH-TIME.
SPLOT
NO SALT FOR YOU, DAUGHTER OF MINE. IT'S BAD FOR YOU.
IT'S GOOD FOR THE TASTE, THOUGH.
TRY PEPPER INSTEAD.
WH? AAH . . .
SNIFF
SNIFF
SNIFF
A A AH...AH...A...A...A...A...A...
CHOO
SPLAT
BLUG!

WATCH OUT! YOU'LL MAKE ME . . .
DOOH! YOU CAN KEEP YOUR PEPPER, PAL.
CLONK!
A...A...A...A...A...A...A...A...A...A
Ooo
CHOO!
SNEEZE?
THUD
OOF! NO THANKS. JUST HAD ONE.
ALL ABOARD.
AAAAAAAAAA

CHOO!
WHEEE!
GIDDUP, DOBBIN-DAD.
ACHOO
ACHOO
ACHOO
ACHOO!
ACHOO!
YEEHAR!
ACHOO
ROYAL ASKALOT (Race Course)
ACHOO
I SAY!

DUCK
SPORT TV
ACHOO
ACHOO
ACHOO
ACHOO ACHOO
ACHOO
ACHOO
ACHOO
ACHOO
CORKS!
ACHOO!
FASTER, POPS!
NEIGH!
TA, MISSUS! COOL TROPHY.
AACHOO! AACHOO!
SNATCH
ACHOO
ACHOO

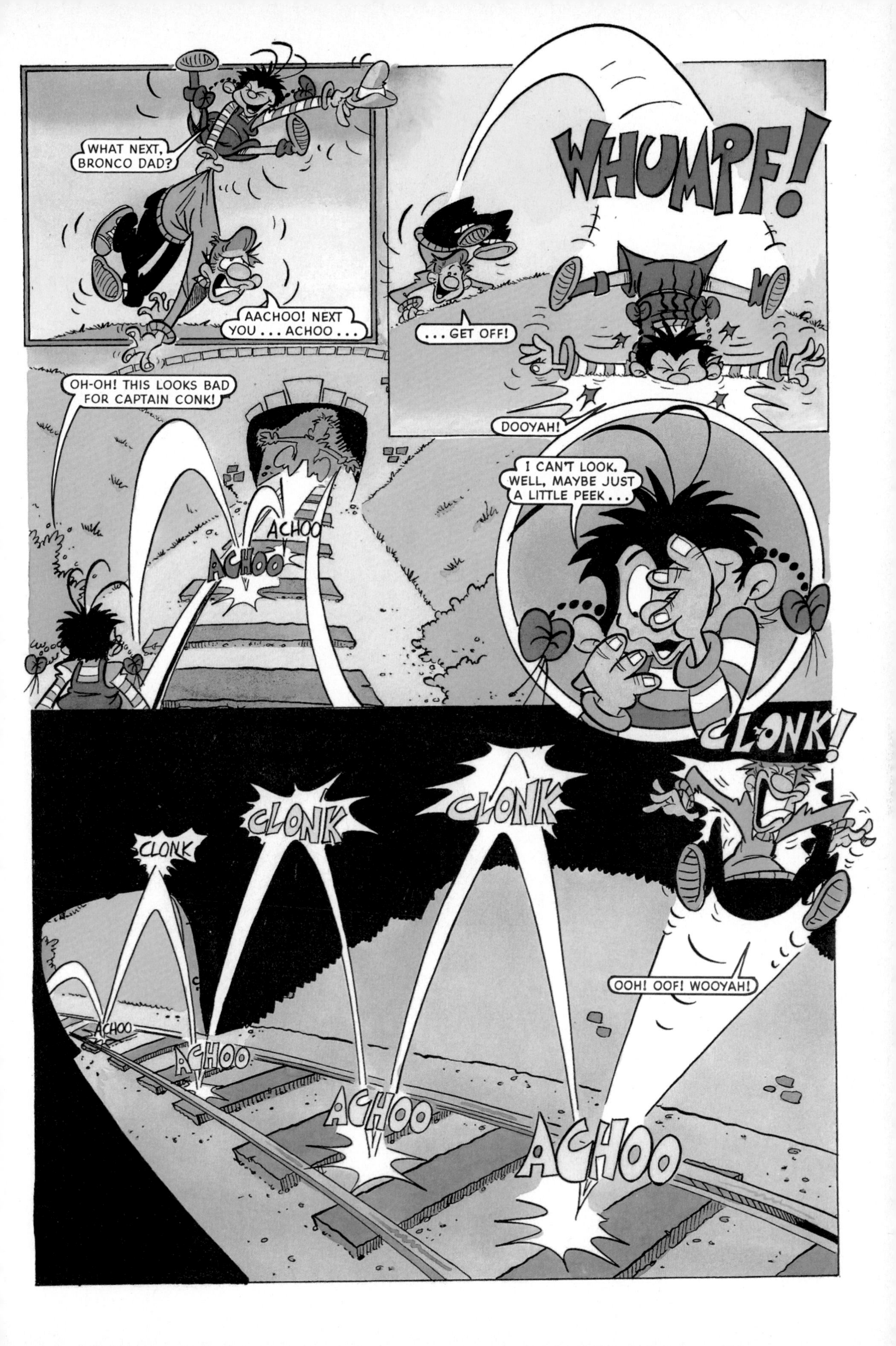
WHAT NEXT, BRONCO DAD?
AACHOO! NEXT YOU . . . ACHOO . . .
WHUMPF!
. . . GET OFF!
DOOYAH!
OH-OH! THIS LOOKS BAD FOR CAPTAIN CONK!
ACHOO
ACHOO
I CAN'T LOOK. WELL, MAYBE JUST A LITTLE PEEK . . .
CLONK!
CLONK
CLONK
CLONK
OOH! OOF! WOOYAH!
ACHOO
ACHOO
ACHOO
ACHOO

ACHOO
OH-OH! THE SNEEZER'S OUT OF CONTROL.
GOTTA GET HOME BEFORE BEAKY . . .
ACHOO
KER-SPLAT
. . . TO OPEN THE DOOR FOR HIM.
ACHOO!
SQUEAK!
S-SEE? I T-TOLD YOU PEPPER WAS B-BETTER FOR YOU.
LOOKS LIKE OL' POP'S BEEN A-SALT-ED!

KORKY and the KITS
COUSIN KONKY'S INVITED YOU THREE TO VISIT HIS FARM.
YES!
OH, BOY!
WHOOPEE!
ER — WHAT'S A FARM?
A PLACE WITH LOTS OF LIVESTOCK, SILLY-BILLIES!
WE'VE GOT OUR KITBAGS — 'BYE, UNCLE KORKY.
'BYE.
Soon —
KONKYS FARM
HI, KITS — BET YOU CAN'T WAIT TO SEE THE LIVESTOCK,
YOU BET RIGHT, UNCLE KONKY.

So —
GOSH! WHAT ARE YOU?
I'M A GOOSE, YOU SILLY GEESE.
GEE! GEESE SURE WALK FUNNY.
THEY DO.
OH, YES — THEY DO.
ARE YOU THINKING WHAT I'M THINKING?
I AM.
ME TOO!
HEH! HEH!
HA! HA!
HEE! HEE!
WHO CHORTLES?

BUMP! BUMP! BUMP!
AHA!
HELP!
HISS!
HISS! HISS! I'LL TEACH YOU NOT TO TAKE THE — HISSS! — MICKEY OUT OF ME!
?
WHAT?
GRUMP!
Later —
HE WALKS FUNNY AS WELL.
SNIGGER!

HEH! HEH! NOT ONLY DOES HE WALK FUNNY, HE CAN'T CLIMB EITHER!
GRRR!
Then —
BOING!
BOING!
WOW! THEY WALK THE FUNNIEST OF ALL THE LIVESTOCK!
BOING!
BOING!
BOING!
BAHH! THAT'S NOT AMUSING!
BAAH!
MEEOW!
CRASH!
BUT THAT WAS!

After a trip to the vets...
GEE! YOU GUYS SURE WALK FUNNY!
STAGGER!
THROB!
LIMP!
HOBBLE!
THROB! ACHE!
R.T. NIXON

OWEN GOAL

GOALS SCORED THIS SEASON
FOR 1
AGAINST
CONTINUED ON NEXT WALL
COACH
MILK + 6 SUGARS PLEASE, BEFORE YOU KNOCK!
TRANSFERS?
WHAT'S THIS?

FREE TRANSFERS? YOU'RE ON!
COACH OF THE YEAR AWARD 1987
REVOKED 1988
OH-OH! BETTER WARN THE LADS.
OWEN GOAL
FOR 1
OWN 66
EXPLODED 3
EVAPORATED 1
DISALLOWED 436

THE COACH IS GOING TO GIVE US ALL FREE TRANSFERS!!!
SMIRKY NOT INCLUDED
GIBBER! GIBBER!
EEK!
OH, PANTS! LET'S BE DEAD NICE TO HIM . . . HE MIGHT CHANGE HIS MIND!
PANIC STATION

NOTICE: COACH IS ALWAYS RIGHT! EXCEPT WHEN HE'S WRONG, WHEN HE'S EXTRA RIGHT!!
60 WATT BULB
LEAGUE LADDER
GASP! WHAT IS GOING ON?
JUST BEING OUR USUAL HELPFUL SELVES, WONDERFUL BOSS.
WE OUR COACH
CUSTARD + CURRANT CAKES
LOVELY HOT LARD PIES
I SAY GIVE HIM A KNIGHTHOOD!
SIMPER!
POLISH
TACKS
CAN I HAVE YOUR AUTOGRAPH, COACH? YOU'RE SUCH A STAR.

WOULD YOU LOT BEAT IT . . . OH! AND SHOW THAT DELIVERY BOY IN!
DANDYTOW F.C UNDER 13s FOOTBALL TRAINING GROUND
SIGH! HE DOESN'T LOVE US ANY MORE.

DRAT! STICKY BUSINESS THESE TRANSFERS.
DOOM!
COACH AND YELLING AT THE TEAM CHAMPION, 1998
HE'S STILL TALKING TRANSFERS. WE'VE GOT TO GIVE IT ONE MORE GO, LADS. CHANGE HIS MIND.

COACH WHEN HE WAS TOP GOALSCORER DANDYTOWN UNDER-25s, 1972-73 SEASON
BAH! NO WONDER THESE TRANSFERS WERE FREE FROM THE NEWSAGENTS . . . HALF OF THEM DON'T WORK!
STICK ON TRANSFERS???
FOOTY
FREE TRANSFERS
MICHAEL OWEN!

GRR! WHAT A FRIGHT TO GIVE US OVER NOTHING!
YEAH! LET'S STICK IT TO HIM WITH THESE STICKERS!
YELP! WHAT DID I DO?

Winker Watson
I'VE JUST PAINTED AN OLD MASTER. HO-HO-HO!
CREEPY by ME

I'M VERY UNHAPPY AT THIS SCHOOL. I DON'T SEE ANYTHING TO LAUGH AT.
AH! YOU'RE THE NEW BOY.

LOOK, PAL! I'M THE CHIEF WANGLER AT GREYTOWERS. I'LL SOON CHEER YOU UP.
OH? HOW?

"EVEN IN NORMAN TIMES THERE WERE SAD CHILDREN."
THIS DAY, VERILY, WE WILL CONSTRUCT BOWS AND ARROWS.
GREYTOWERS SCHOOL
Lesson for today
NORMAN
NORMAN
NORMAN
THE GOOD TEACHER CREEP IS TRULY A BIG BORE.

"A QUICK WANGLE LATER PUT PAID TO THAT ROTTEN LESSON AND GAVE US ALL A GOOD LAUGH, TOO!"
BOP!
OOPS! SORRY, SIRE. MY ARROW WENT AWRY.
YE ARCHERY LESSON
HE MEANT THAT AWRY'M A MONKEY'S UNCLE.

SEE! THERE HAVE BEEN GOOD WANGLERS AND GREAT FUN HERE FOR YEARS AND YEARS.
HUH! SO YOU SAY.

"EVEN IN THE STONE AGE!"
PREHISTORIC GREYSTONE SCHOOL CLUBBING LESSON
THIS IS HOW A CLUB WORKS. USE THE HEAD.
BAM!
MAYBE I SHOULDN'T HAVE USED HIS HEAD BUT I'VE WANGLED US SOME TIME OFF. TEE-HEE!
HA-HA!
OOH! PRETTY STARS.
WE WANGLERS WERE AROUND EVEN AT THE TIME OF CROMWELL.
EH?
HAND OVER YOUR SWORD, SIR CREEPWELL. YOU LOST — WE WON.
WE'LL LEAVE HIM HANGING AROUND WHILE WE POP OFF FOR SOME TUCK, TROTTY.
GOOD IDEA!
MY GRANDFATHER WAS HERE DURING THE WAR WHEN THE SCHOOL WAS TAKEN OVER BY THE SECRET SERVICE.
OH, YES?
"GRANDPA TOOK HIS WANGLING SERIOUSLY."
THUD!
TRAINING SESSION MR W. WATSON
NASTY SPIES MUST BE BOOTED OUT OF BRITAIN — JUST LIKE THAT.

I WANGLE WHENEVER I CAN — AND THIS IS A GOOD TIME FOR A WHEEZE.
AAIIEEE!
OO-ER! HOW DOES ONE STOP A THING LIKE THIS?
YOU SHOULD BE MORE CAREFUL, SIR. IT'S SILLY TO PLAY WITH SKATEBOARDS AT YOUR AGE.
BASEMENT ENTRANCE
OOH! WHERE AM I?
CREEPY ISN'T THE DAFTEST TEACHER TO BE AT GREYTOWERS. ONE EVEN USED THE LIBRARY.
LIBRARY
WHAT'S DAFT ABOUT THAT?
"WELL, HE'D MADE A SECRET ROOM BEHIND THE BOOKCASES."
OO-ER! THOSE HAIRY SCOTS ARE RAIDING AGAIN. I'D BETTER GO TO MY SECRET HIDING PLACE — QUICK!
COME BACK HERE, YE SPECKY, WEE SASSENACH!

AND HE'S STILL HERE. HE FORGOT TO PUT A HANDLE ON THE INSIDE OF THE DOOR.
CLICK!
OOH!
RUMBLE!

NOW I'LL SHOW YOU A REAL WANGLER'S ESCAPE ROUTE. FOLLOW ME.
SCHOOL KITCHEN

HELLO! SOMEONE'S USING THE DUMB WAITER.
RUMBLE! RUMBLE!

YOU PULL THIS ROPE AND UP WE GO.

AND WHEN WE COME TO THE TOP, WE MAKE SURE NOBODY FOLLOWS US.
SOOT

NOW WHAT D'YOU THINK OF THAT FOR A SOOT-ABLE WANGLE?
BOOMPH!

A LITTLE WHILE AGO, WE HAD A POTTY SCIENCE TEACHER HERE.

VATCH VILE I AM TESTING MEIN NEW ROCKET FUEL.
I THINK IT'S TIME TO LEAVE, CHAPS.

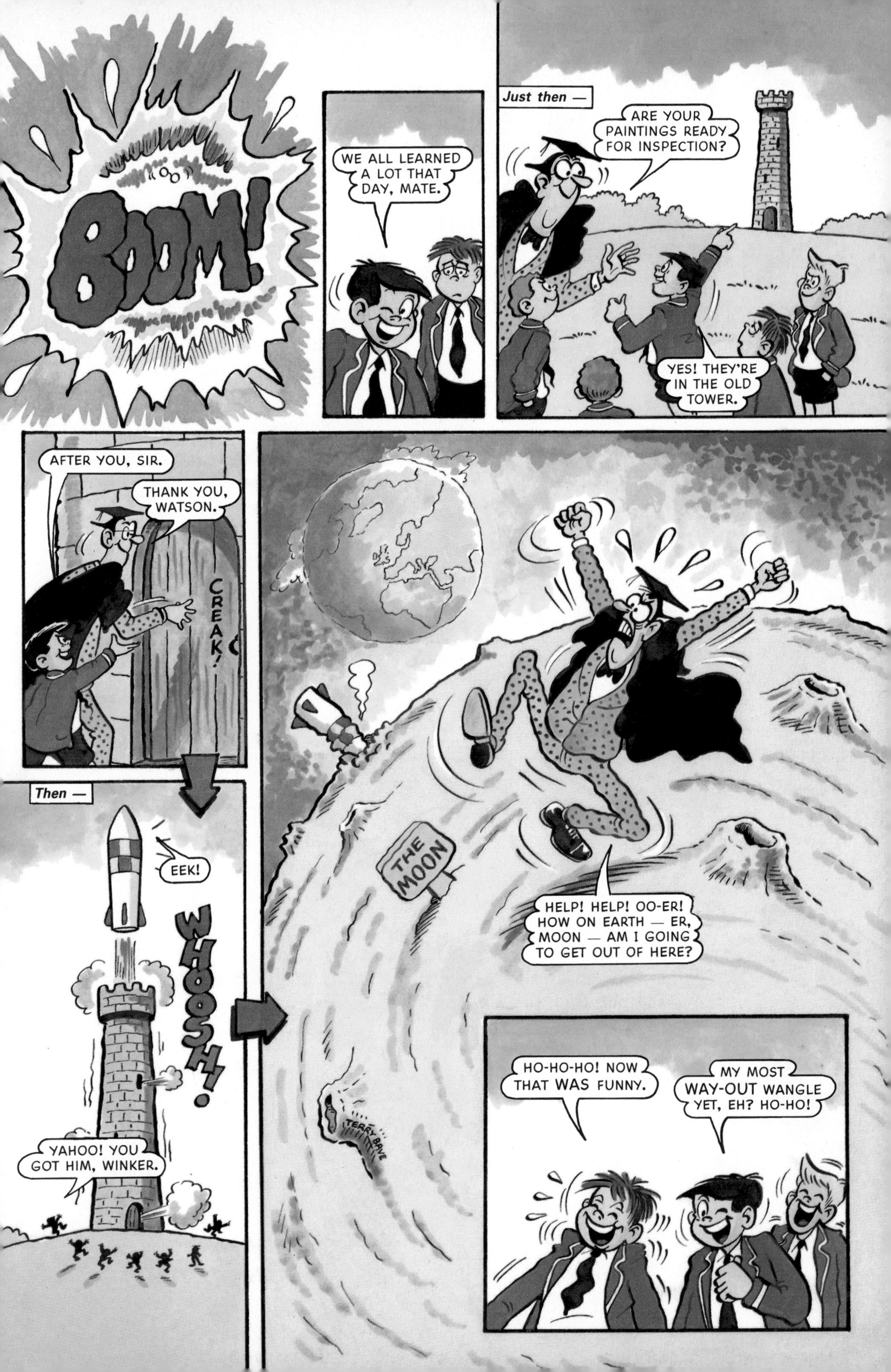
"OOO"
BOOM!
WE ALL LEARNED A LOT THAT DAY, MATE.
Just then —
ARE YOUR PAINTINGS READY FOR INSPECTION?
YES! THEY'RE IN THE OLD TOWER.
AFTER YOU, SIR.
THANK YOU, WATSON.
CREAK!
Then —
EEK!
WHOOSH!
YAHOO! YOU GOT HIM, WINKER.
THE MOON
HELP! HELP! OO-ER! HOW ON EARTH — ER, MOON — AM I GOING TO GET OUT OF HERE?
HO-HO-HO! NOW THAT WAS FUNNY.
MY MOST WAY-OUT WANGLE YET, EH? HO-HO!
TERRY BAVE

BODKIN'S MOOR
BOK!
Steven Stickleback the aquatic quarterback
American Football is not a game usually associated with the babbling brooks of Britain, but Steven the three-spined stickleback was a huge fan.
He had painstakingly put together an all star team of pond life in the stream that runs through Farmer Bodkin's lower meadow. Daphne the water flea was a wide receiver, Bubba the water boatman was a tight end and Steven himself was a quarterback stickleback.

Obviously, Steven had had to modify the rules somewhat. Three was not an ideal number for a team and the fact that none of them had hands made ball handling difficult. What made it extra difficult was the fact that they didn't have a ball. Steven had compromised by using a piece of gravel and he threw it by flicking it with his tail. Bubba would then catch it on his back before passing it to Daphne who would then kick it through the stalks of pondweed that served as a goal.
WHACK!
DONK!
BOOT!
This unorthodox arrangement worked well and the Aquatic All Stars were undefeated in three seasons. This encouraged Tanya the tadpole to form a group of cheerleaders and at every game the agile amphibians would wiggle bits of fluff like pom-poms. There was one drawback, however (no — a drawback is not a position in an American Football team) and that was because there were no other teams in the brook. Winning games without opposition was becoming boring for Steven.
1
CHAMPS

With a flash of inspiration and a dash of perspiration Steven had a brilliant idea. Why not have an underwater version of the Super Bowl? Quickly he spread the word round the waterways, looking for teams to contest the Bodkin's Moor Fish Bowl. The response was phenomenal — one other team entered. The team called itself the Piratical Pikes and consisted of one large pike called Philip. A group of football-loving water snails marked out the pitch and, with Tanya's tadpoles cheering from the sidelines, the teams took the field.

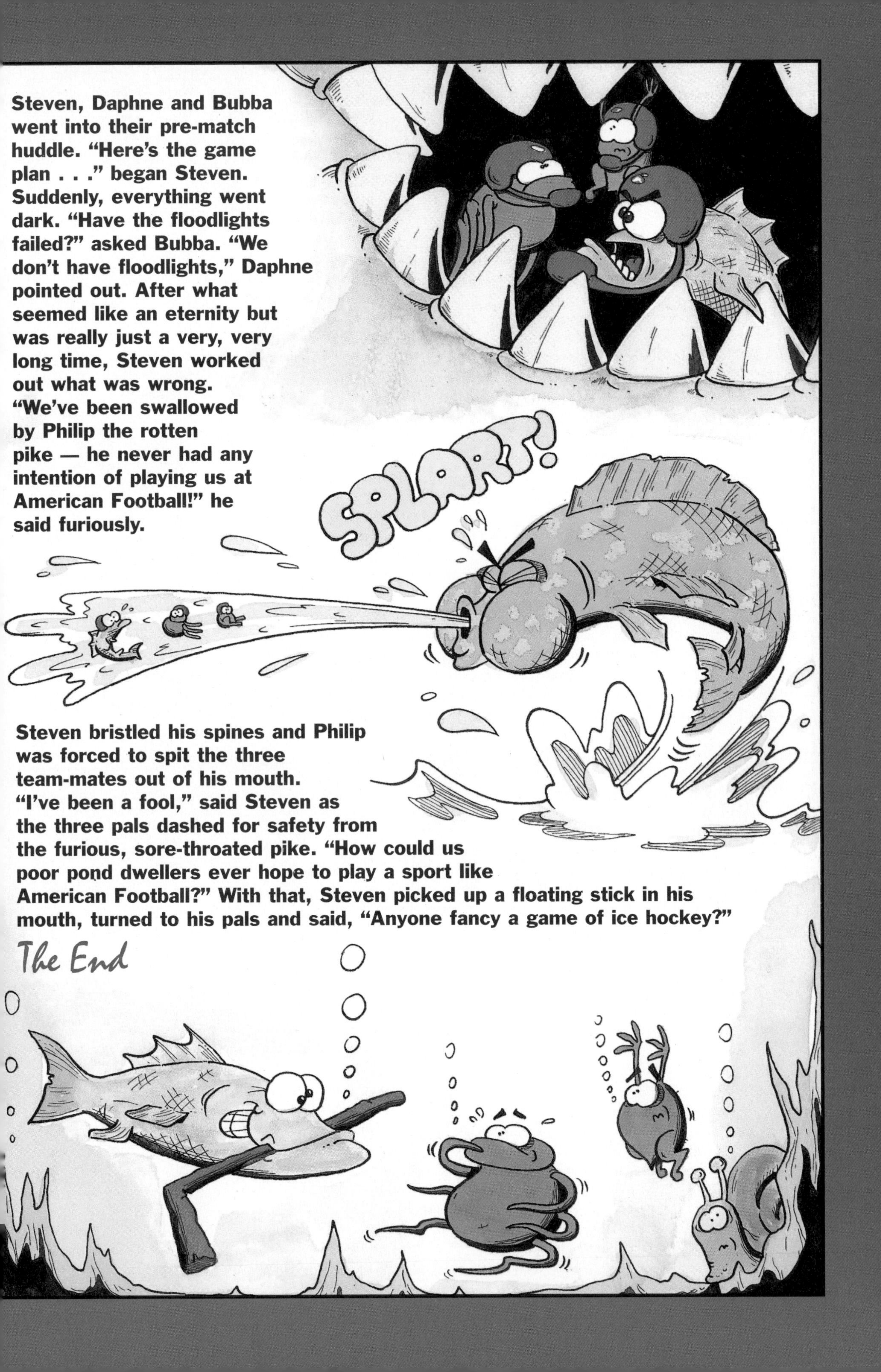

Steven, Daphne and Bubba went into their pre-match huddle. "Here's the game plan . . ." began Steven. Suddenly, everything went dark. "Have the floodlights failed?" asked Bubba. "We don't have floodlights," Daphne pointed out. After what seemed like an eternity but was really just a very, very long time, Steven worked out what was wrong. "We've been swallowed by Philip the rotten pike — he never had any intention of playing us at American Football!" he said furiously.

Steven bristled his spines and Philip was forced to spit the three team-mates out of his mouth. "I've been a fool," said Steven as the three pals dashed for safety from the furious, sore-throated pike. "How could us poor pond dwellers ever hope to play a sport like American Football?" With that, Steven picked up a floating stick in his mouth, turned to his pals and said, "Anyone fancy a game of ice hockey?"

The End

THE GREAT YETI HUNT

Out among the craggy mountains of the Himalayas, a wild howl cuts through the freezing air. Is it some wild beast?
HHHOOOWWLLL

No, it's Marcel Darcel — Yeti hunter and idiot.
FULL
WILD? I AM ZE LIVID! ZE SEAT IN 'ERE IS FREEZING!

BUT 'AVE NO FEAR, MY LITTLE READER-TYPE CHUMS, FOR I, ZE BRAVE MARCEL AM GOING YETI-HUNTING.

AHA! ZIS LOOKS LIKE ZE FOOTPRINT OF A YETI.
YUP!

AND IF ZERE IS A YETI NEAR HERE . . .
YUP!
. . . I WILL CATCH HEEM IN MA YETI-TRAP — AND SELL HIM TO A ZOO FOR LOADS OF FRANCS.

FIRST, I WILL SET A TRAIL OF GRUB FOR ZE . . .

DUNT!
OOF!

. . . YETI?

YETI!
YUP!

EET'S ZE ABONINIMABIBBLE SNOWMAN. EEK.
CARAMBA!

YUP!
WELL, AT LEAST NOW I KNOW MY TRAP WORKS. I WILL BE BACK.
Y*P!

So —
I AM NOW ZE SNEAKY HUNTER. I WEEL CAPTURE ZE DOZY LITTLE BABY YETI AND GET ZE ZOO'S LOOT.
$m^c = \sqrt[2]{\frac{x-3{\cdot}07}{ab^{-3}}}$

ZE QUIETLY — AND SNEAKILY — DOES IT.
OR PERHAPS
$\frac{-16^2}{9} \times \sqrt{\frac{17}{ab^3}}$

ONE SWIPE OF ZE NET AND VOILA — NABBED!
NO, I TELL A LIE - $x = mc^2$

ZE OH, KNICKERS.
YUP!

ZE EXCUSE ME, MONSIEUR LE YETI. WOULD YOU MIND GOING TO ZE ZOO, PLEASE?
YUP!
NOW DON'T FEED THE HUMAN, JUNIOR. IT'S NOT CAVE-TRAINED.
ER, ZIS ISN'T EXACTLY WHAT I HAD IN MIND . . .
COO! FANCY HAVING NO FUR. CHILLY.
HUMAN (THICK)

DESPERATE DAN
NO WONDER AUNT AGGIE GETS ME TO DO THE SHOPPING!
special COW-PIE GRAVY MIX
OWL HOOT JUICE -6- PACK
FLOUR

CACTUSVILLE HYPERMARKET
CAR PARK
THIS WEEK'S BARGAINS:
THANKS FOR COMING, DAN — I NEED YOUR HELP!
SURE THING, MR STORE BOSS.

TROLLEY PARK
OUR TROLLEYS ARE DISAPPEARING!

YEEHA!
WHIZZ!
SMASH!
THERE GOES ANOTHER ONE!
I'LL SOON HAVE THEM OFF YOUR TROLLEY!

SPEEDY
TRUNDLE!
YIPPEE! I'LL SOON CATCH 'EM!
GIDDY-UP, TROLLEY!
CACTUSVILLE CANYON
SCOOT!

WAIT THERE, YOUNG VARMINTS!
WHOOSH!
NO CHANCE! WE'RE OFF!
58

THIS THUMP IS A PAIN IN THE RUMP!
CRUMPAH!
AHEM! MAYBE THE TROLLEY FELT IT MORE THAN ME!
Then —
RATTLE!
TRUNDLE!
LOOKS LIKE I'VE DISCOVERED WHERE THOSE TROLLEYS HAVE BEEN GOIN'! SOME SNEAKY MINERS ARE USING THEM TO CLEAR OUT THEIR TUNNELS!

And—
LOOK AT THEM WAGONS HEADING WEST!
WOW! LOOK AT THEM TROLLEYS HEADING EAST!
ERMARKET
SIDE ENTRANCE
WELL DONE, DAN! PUSH THEM IN HERE!
TRUNDLE!
CRASH!
RATTLE!
SLOWLY, DAN! SLOWLY!
CRUSH!

PLEASE TAKE A TROLLEY
Cola 20p OFF
Tissues ON OFFER
MAGAZINES
PUSH!
HEAVE!
LEVER!
WAP!
TOOLS
WE'VE GOT OUR TROLLEY'S BACK — BUT NO-ONE CAN USE THEM!
CHEEK!
TODAY'S BEST BUY BAD GUY
T'AIN'T MY FAULT YOUR CUSTOMERS ARE SO PUNY!
CALUORI

HAMISH the HAGGIS-BASHER...
A Hairy Caledonian Fantasy!
Long, long ago in the bonnie Scottish Highlands.it was a peaceful morning . . .
BONNIE SCOTLAND FOREVERRR! HOOTS!
BEN McTUMSHIE
OINK! BLEAT! MOOO!
VERY RARE HAIRY CALEDONIAN RHINOCEROS, THE NOO.
SQUAWK! HOOTS!
LOCH McTUMSHIE
McTUMSHIE FALLS
GIANT HEILAN HAGGIS
BURRP! BELCH! THE NOO!
THISTLE JUICE YE KEN
ROAAAR!
STEAMIN' HOT KIPPER-INFESTED COCKALEEKIE BURN
HAGGIS BURGER
QUACK! QUACK! THE NOO!
WELCOME TAE GLEN McTUMSHIE THE NOO.
NAE PINCHIN' THE HEATHER!
OCH! SEE YOU, JIMMY!
RARE HAIRY RASPBERRY-BLOWING KIPPER.
RARE HAIRY SCOTTISH DUCK.
RAAAZPLE! THRRAAARRT!

. . . until a wild roar broke the calm.
CHIEF'S HOOSEY
BELLOW!
CHIEF'S BREEKS
But it wasn't a wild beast — it was Chief McTumshie of McTumshie.
AND WHAUR'S MA BREAKFAST?
BANG
THUD!

AHA! THERE'S HAMISH — THE LAZY WEE BAUCHLE WHO'S SUPPOSED TAE COOK MA BREKKIES.
HEILAN' COO
Hoots! It's a braw, bricht moonlicht nicht the nicht! Och, aye, Jimmy!
PORRIDGE
THISTLE JUICE
EMERGENCY NIGHT-TIME PORRIDGE SUPPLY
HAMISH'S PIT.
HAMISH

OOT O' YER PIT, LADDIE.
HOOF!
OOYAH!
AND DINNAE COME BACK WITHOOT MA BREAKFAST.
FAMISHED FUME!
MUTTER. McGRUMBLE.
HOOTS THE NOO!
PORR

I'LL GET THE CHIEFY A MUCKLE BIG DOLLOP O' HIS FAVOURITE PORRIDGE.
OINK!
NATURAL BOILIN' PORRIDGE PITS, (THE NOO!)
BLUP!
YIKES!
HONK!
LEAP!
UGH!
SPLEURGE!
SNORT!
DRAT! IT'S A FLIPPIN' CHEEKY WEE HAGGIS.
HONK.
STOP PLAYIN' IN MAH FOOD AND GO CATCH ME A FRESH HAGGIS.
PLUCK!
RIGHTO, CHIEFY.
DRIP!
TOOT!

AN' DINNAE MESS UP THIS TIME.
BOOT!
SCOTCH BROTH BOG.
BLOOP!
BOYLK!
RIGHT. I'VE GOT A CUNNING PLAN. IT'S BRILLIANT . . .
CLACK!
CLICK!
DINKLE!
HAGGIS HATCHERY.
GOO-GOO THE NOO!
. . . SNEAK UP ON THEM AN' GUB ONE WI' MA HAGGIS-BASHER.
YE ANCIENT CLAN HAGGIS-BASHER.
DIABOLICAL CACKLE!
TIPPYTOE!
OH-OH! WHIT'S THIS?
TRIP!
OOYAH! RIGHT IN THE SPORRAN. YEOW!
SNIGGLE!
SNEEGER!
PAINFUL PRANG IN THE PANTS!
LEGENDARY GIANT HAGGIS OF GLEN McTUMSHIE.
BASH! CRUNCH!
HOOT!
SPROING! FEPTAANG!

OOH! EEH! OOHOO! THAT FAIR HURT!
TRIUMPHANT TOOTLE!
Soon—
I'LL GET A HAGGIS YET! NOW WHAT DO HAGGISES LIKE?
OCH! SEE YON HAGGIS, JIMMY!
OF COURSE! THEY LIKE OTHER HAGGISES!
DRESSED LIKE THIS I CAN JUST WANDER UP AN' GRAB ONE!
SNEAKY SNIGGER!
McTUMSHIE'S FANCY DRESS HIRE
HAIRY HIGHLAND HAGGIS COSTUME
TUM-TI-TUM . . .
McTUMSHIE'S FANCY DRESS.
RUSTLE!
HAGGIS HATCHERY.
SWIPE!
GOTCHA!
MASH! BASH! BLOOTER!

OOR BELOVED CHIEFY
SLAVER!
SLABBER!
BURBLE!
McTUMSHIE'S COSTUME HIRE
CHIEF'S BIB YE KEN
WHAT A MUCKLE, BIG HAGGIS! WHAT FINE!
TATTIES
NEEPS
CHOMP!
YEEOOWW!
WHEECH!
BADLY BITTEN BOTTY!

LUCKY WHITE HEATHER, THE NOO!
THUDD!
OOFYABOY!
CHIEFY WILL JIST HAVE TO MAKE DO WI' PORRIDGE FOR BREAKFAST.
PUFF! PECH!
CHIEF'S PORRIDGE, OCH AYE!
EXCEPT YOU'VE TAKEN SO BLUMMIN' LONG IT'S DINNER-TIME NOW, SO GET ME MA DINNER.
OCH, JINGS, CRIVVENS AND HELP MA BOAB!
FINE! I'LL GET YER DINNER BUT YE CAN COOK IT YERSELF!
CHIEFY'S HOOSEY
HUFFY HUMPH!
FINE!
HERE Y'ARE, CHIEFY — NICE AN' FRESH.
MOO-OOO!
SNORT!
LEAP!
FRILLY UNDER SPORRAN
CHIEFY'S BREEKS
McYIKES.
THARRUMPH!

CREATURE FEATURES

TIK AND TAK
YES!
PACK AWAY YOUR TOYS. WE'VE COPPED FOR A DAY OUT.
CAN I BRING MY YO-YO?
WHAT DID HE SAY, TAK?
HE SAID IT'S A COPS' DAY OUT!
NO NEED TO SHOUT!
COPS NEED A BREAK AFTER CATCHING CROOKS AND ROBBERS.
COO!
RIGHT, MATE. YOU'RE NICKED.
EEK! IT'S A 'FAIR' COP!
MEE-MAW!
WOO-WOO!
THAT'S WHY THEY HAVE A COPS' DAY OUT. THEY'RE ALLOWED TO BELT UP AND DOWN THE MOTORWAYS.

Later, at a local park —
RIGHT, LADS. HERE WE ARE.
GO-KARTING! CLAY PIGEON SHOOTING! BUGGIES!
I HOPE THIS COPS' DAY OUT IS GOOD.
IT IS NOT A COPS' DAY OUT, OKAY?
LET'S TRY GO-KARTING FIRST.
KARTING
PHOOWEE! TOUCHY, ISN'T HE?
POSITIVELY GRUMPY.
STADIUM
WE'LL BEAT YOU TO THE FINISH.
NO WAY!
OLLY OILS
TOM TYRES
YIKES! HE'S FAST!
AND DANGEROUS!
HAR-HAR! I'LL DRIVE THOSE LITTLE HORRORS INTO THE GROUND.
MOTOR

GRR! I'M GETTING ANNOYED AT HIS SMUG, SMILING FACE.
HO-HO! CAN'T CATCH ME.
WHAP!
ROAR!
I'LL TAKE A SHORT-CUT.
YEEKS!
THAT'S GOT HIM IN A SPIN.
NOW, IT'S MY TURN.
OOH! AAH!
I'M A GOOD PENALTY TAKER.
WHAM!
CRASH!
OOF!

OUT, YOU VANDALS.
EEK!
OW!
BANG BANG
CLAY PIGEON SHOOTING
DOH! NOISY THINGS.
LET'S TRY THE BUGGIES.
BUGGIES
Then —
YAHOO!
YARROO!
WHEEE!
GERONIMO!
WHAT'S ALL THAT NOISE ABOUT?
ROAR
VAROOMEN!
AARGH!
NICE DRIVING, OLD BUDDY.
WHOA! STOP!
BUZZZT!
WAHEY!
HOWL!

Meanwhile —
I'LL TRY MY HAND AT CLAY PIGEON SHOOTING.
PULL!
WHANG!
Suddenly —
BANZAI!
BOOM BOOM
WHEEE!
BRROOM
ROAR!
GLOOP!
WOOSH!
WOOSH!
GRR! THAT DOES IT!
DRIP!
GLOOP!

COME BACK, YOU LITTLE MONSTERS!
NOT LIKELY!
IT'S TIME WE SPLIT.
SPLIT!
GOOD IDEA!
EEK! WHERE'D THEY GO?
BUZZ!
Then —
CRASH!
WEEE!
SPLUTTER! D'YOU SEE THAT? AN ARMED ROBBER.
ER — THIS ISN'T WHAT YOU THINK.
MEE-MAW! MEE-MAW!
AFTER HIM!
HELP!
POLICE
SEE? IT'S JUST LIKE I SAID. IT'S A 'COPS' DAY OUT'.

GROWING PAYNES

PERCY SHOULD BE BACK HOME . . .

. . . SOON!
OUT OF THE WAY!

I'D BETTER HURRY.
WHAT'S ALL THE RUSH?

PERCY! WHAT'S WRONG? ARE YOU FEELING ILL?
GO AWAY! I'M NOT TALKING TO YOU. I MUST GET TO SLEEP.

WHAT'S WRONG WITH THE LITTLE PEST?
I DON'T KNOW. MAYBE HE'S FALLEN OUT WITH A GIRLFRIEND OR SOMETHING.

THEY PROBABLY WOULDN'T LET HIM PLAY WITH THEIR SOPPY DOLLS.
MAYBE YOU'RE RIGHT, PETER.

CLUNK!
I HEARD THAT!
OUCH!

SLAM!
NOW LEAVE ME ALONE!
GOODNESS! HE REALLY IS IN A BAD MOOD.

Soon after —
TEA'S UP.
YUM-YUM! I'LL GET PERCY'S AS WELL.

Suddenly —
WAAGGHH!
AAGH!
OH! THAT'S MY POOR BABY.

I'VE RUN OUT OF PAPER!
OO-ER!
OH, DEAR! HE'S GOT A BAD TUMMY.

DID YOU EAT SOMETHING BAD AT SCHOOL THAT'S UPSET YOUR TUM?
NO! BUT I **AM** VERY UPSET.

SO YOU WON'T NEED THIS LITTLE LOT, THEN?
NO! AND I DON'T NEED MUM HERE EITHER.

COME ON, PERCY. TELL BIG BROTHER WHAT'S WRONG.

MUM'S BEEN KEEPING A SECRET FROM ME.
ME? A SECRET? WHAT DO YOU MEAN?

YOU DIDN'T TELL ME SANTA IS COMING TONIGHT. I HAVEN'T HAD TIME TO WRITE TO HIM YET.
SANTA? HE'S NOT COMING YET. WHERE'D YOU GET THAT IDEA?

I'LL SHOW YOU. SOMEBODY'S BEEN TELLING PORKIES.
WAIT! GET DRESSED FIRST.
WHERE ARE WE GOING?
BACK DOWN SCHOOL ROAD.
AKER
T'S

Café del Splendor
SEE? WE HAVE CHRISTMAS DINNER JUST AFTER WE OPEN OUR PREZZIES. SO IT MUST BE TIME FOR SANTA TO COME.
ORDER YOUR CHRISTMAS DINNER NOW!
HMM!

YOU'VE MADE A LITTLE BOY VERY UNHAPPY WITH THAT NOTICE.
OH, DEAR!
THAT JUST MEANS YOU BOOK WELL IN ADVANCE.

Later —
WHAT A KIND MAN. HE'S LETTING US HAVE A FREE, EARLY CHRISTMAS DINNER.
THIS IS COSTING ME A FORTUNE. I'LL JUST PUT AN AD IN THE PAPERS IN FUTURE.
ORDER YOUR CHRIS TMAS DINN NER NO W!

CAT TIPS
A GUIDE TO LIVING FOR TODAY'S CAT
SIGH! US CATS LOVE SLEEPING . . .
. . . ESPECIALLY IN FRONT OF A NICE, WARM FIRE.
'NIGHT ALL. SEE YOU LATER, PEOPLE.

YOO-HOO, PUSS.
AW, WHAT?

PLAY WITH THE BALL OF WOOL. GO ON. PLAY WITH IT.
I HATE IT WHEN HE DOES THAT.

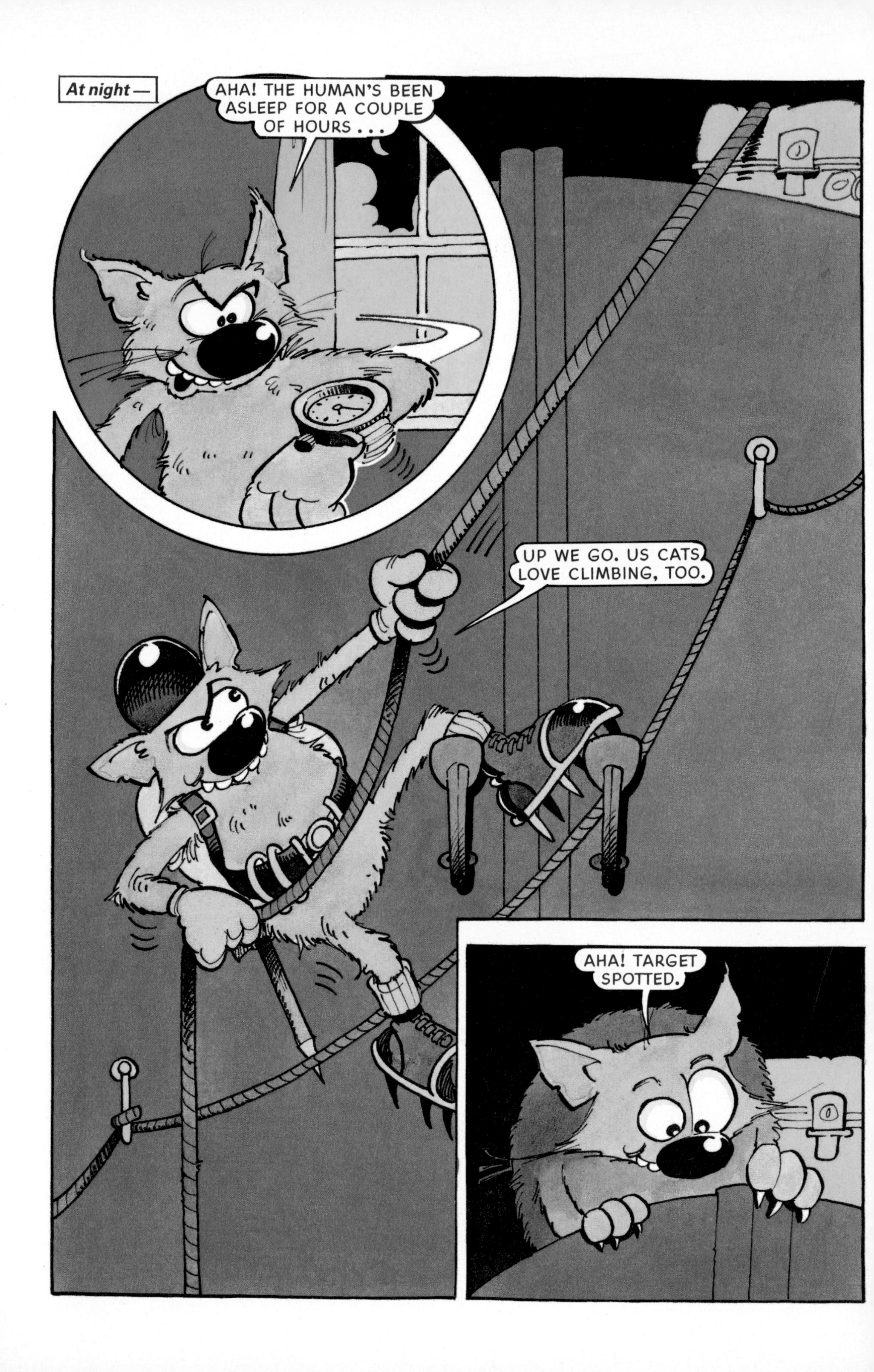

At night —
AHA! THE HUMAN'S BEEN ASLEEP FOR A COUPLE OF HOURS . . .
UP WE GO. US CATS LOVE CLIMBING, TOO.
AHA! TARGET SPOTTED.

GERONIMOGGY!
AAAAARRGH!
WHINE! GIBBER!
THE MORAL OF THIS STORY? LET SLEEPING CATS LIE. PURR.

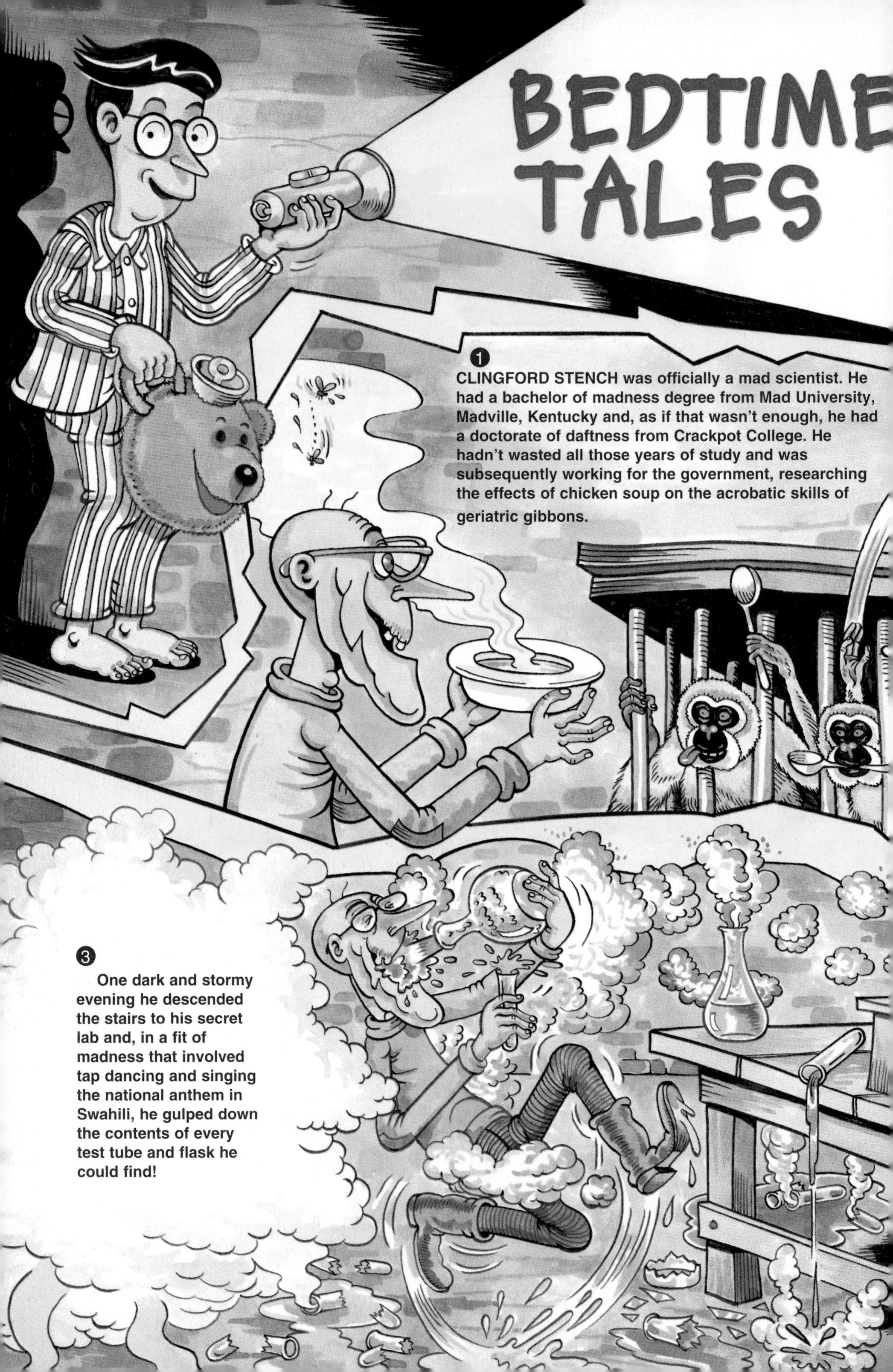
BEDTIME TALES
1
CLINGFORD STENCH was officially a mad scientist. He had a bachelor of madness degree from Mad University, Madville, Kentucky and, as if that wasn't enough, he had a doctorate of daftness from Crackpot College. He hadn't wasted all those years of study and was subsequently working for the government, researching the effects of chicken soup on the acrobatic skills of geriatric gibbons.
3
One dark and stormy evening he descended the stairs to his secret lab and, in a fit of madness that involved tap dancing and singing the national anthem in Swahili, he gulped down the contents of every test tube and flask he could find!

with
Bradley
Bedsock
2
Away from this vital work, Clingford had his own private laboratory in the basement of his creepy, old mansion. It was here that he indulged his passion for potions. He worked out secret formulae for these concoctions — so secret he didn't even let himself know what was in them. His dream was to discover a potion that would restore a thick head of hair to his bulging, balding pate, and had the side effect of making him look less like a startled toad and more like Tom Cruise.
DAVID SUTHERLAND
4
"That's more like it!" I can hear you horror fans thinking. You're expecting him to clutch his throat and begin a hideous transformation from balding egghead to grotesque, hulking, drooling brute. A vicious psychopath who will burst through the laboratory walls and begin a murderous rampage across the storm-lashed city, killing everything in his path.

5
Sadly, for those of us who like to be scared witless, that didn't happen. Clingford simply disappeared. The following day when he didn't show up for work, the geriatric gibbons, desperate for more soup, phoned the police.
7
The collection of chemicals guzzled by the bold Clingford had synthesised in his body and caused a growth of thick, dark hair on his shiny dome. Unfortunately the thick, dark hair didn't confine itself to Mr Stench's head. By using himself as a human guinea pig, the silly scientist had actually transformed himself INTO a guinea pig!

Clingford's
private lab
6
A thorough search was begun and although the police left no stone unturned, the unfortunate Mr Stench remains a missing person. If they hadn't been so busy turning stones the police might have thought to look in Clingford's private lab for there lies the answer to this baffling mystery.
8
To this day, the former brainbox can be found using an exercise wheel in the basement of his creepy mansion, nibbling carrots and shouting "Wheep! Wheep!" at anyone who passes by.
Your bewildered buddy,
Bradley Bedsock.
This story was written by actors and no gibbering geniuses were converted into rodents in the writing of this tale.

FOXY
AH, SPRING — THE BUDS ARE POPPIN' — THE . . .

. . . CHICKENS ARE — ARE — ARE — ARE — DEELISHUS! SLOBBER!
FARM

AN' FARMER'S ON GUARD — FARMER'S ALWAYS ON GUARD!

CLICK!
HOLD ON —
I'M A FOX!

AN' US FOXES ARE
SUPPOSED T' BE
SLY AN' CUNNIN'!
SPRING

SO, BEIN' A SLY
AN' CUNNIN' OLD'
FOXY . . .
SUMMER

. . . I'LL COME UP
WITH A SLY AN'
CUNNIN' PLAN!
AUTUMN

SPRING — THAT'S IT — THAT'S MY SLY AN' CUNNIN' PLAN!
WINTER
I'M GONNA SPRING A SURPRISE ON FARMER AN' THOSE YUMMY CHICKENS.
So—
SNIGGER!
WHASSAT?
TOO LATE, SLOWCOACH.
FOXY!

ER — ANY IDEA HOW I CAN STOP BOUNCIN'?
TUCK YOUR FEET UP TO KEEP THE SPRINGS OFF THE GROUND.
THANKS!
WHAT AN IDIOT!

OOF!
CRASH!

Soon —

HE MAY BE SLY AN' CUNNIN', BUT HE SURE AIN'T VERY CLEVER!
HO-HUM! BACK TO THE DRAWIN' BOARD!

DAN'S DIARY
GOOD NEIGHBOURS DAY
TO SHOW HOW GOOD A NEIGHBOUR I AM I'M GOING TO SHAKE ALL MY NEIGHBOURS BY THE HAND.
THROB!
SHUCKS! I SHOOK THEIR HANDS AND NOW NOBODY LIKES ME AT ALL.
THROB!

The Dandy brings you a special long story . . .
N
W
E
S
NEVILLE'S ISLAND
Young Neville Bird and his family have left the city of Dinchester behind to come and live on picturesque Windy Island. Here Neville begins his new life . . .

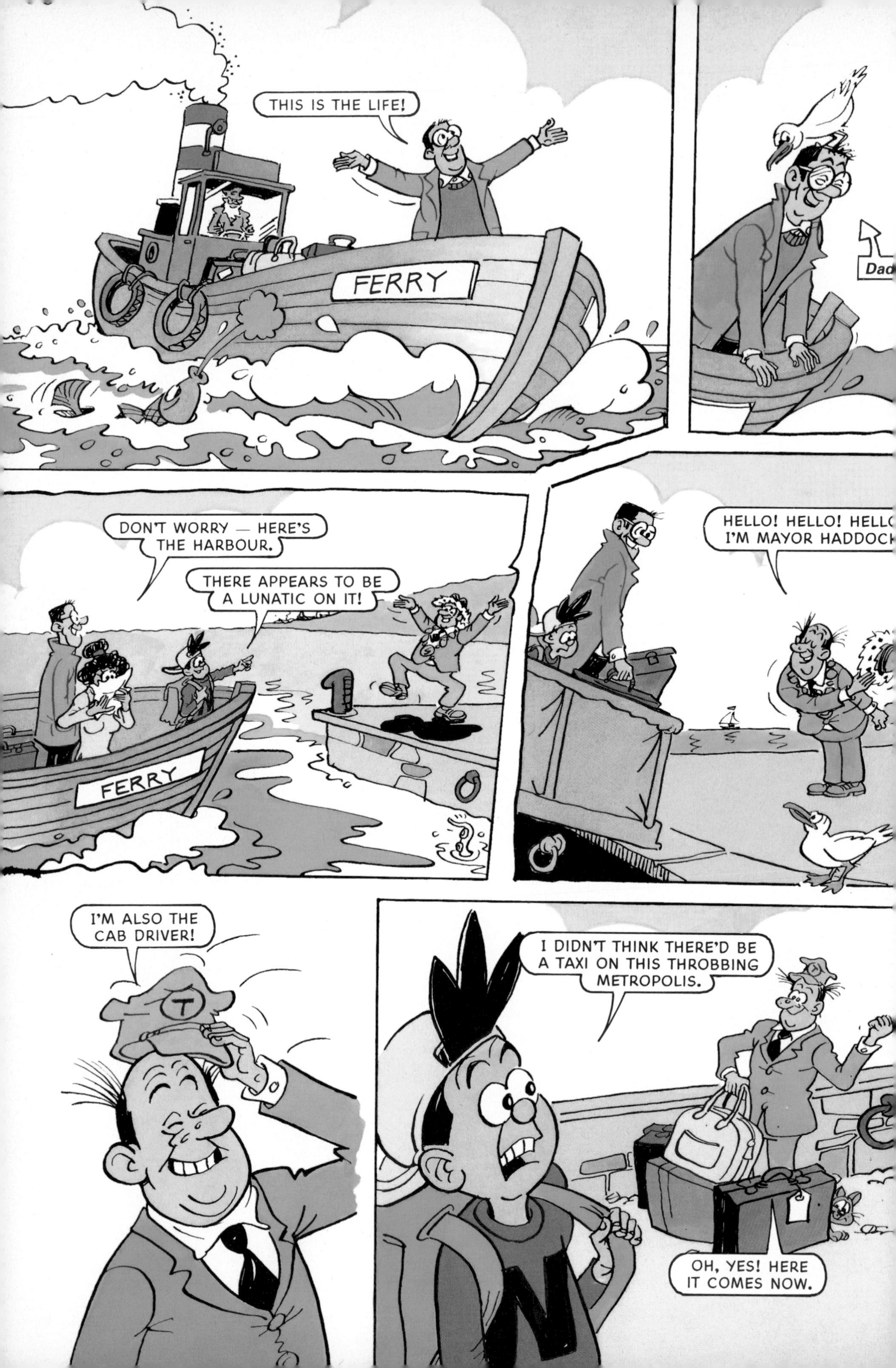
THIS IS THE LIFE!
FERRY
DON'T WORRY — HERE'S THE HARBOUR.
THERE APPEARS TO BE A LUNATIC ON IT!
FERRY
HELLO! HELLO! HELLO
I'M MAYOR HADDOCK
I'M ALSO THE CAB DRIVER!
I DIDN'T THINK THERE'D BE A TAXI ON THIS THROBBING METROPOLIS.
OH, YES! HERE IT COMES NOW.

THE BLUE SKIES, THE WHITE WAVES . . .

THE GREEN FACES!
Neville.

WELCOME TO WINDY ISLAND!

ANY CHANCE OF A TAXI?
SURE!

YOU MUST BE JOKING!
GIDDY-UP, TAXI!
SEA

Shortly —
HERE'S YOUR NEW HOME — CRUMBLY COTTAGE!
CRUMBLY COTTAGE
IT'S LOVELY!
IT'S BEAUTIFUL!
IT STINKS!
IT'S EVEN GOT A GARDEN SHED!
HO-HO! IT'S A FINE SENSE OF HUMOUR YOU CITY FOLK HAVE!
THIS HERE'S YOUR TOILET!
TELL ME I'M DREAMING!

I'LL LEAVE YOU FOLKS TO SETTLE IN. CHEERIO!
THANKS!
FOR NOTHING!
RIGHT! LET'S GET THE TV ON.
ER . . . SORRY, NEV. THERE'S NO ELECTRICITY!
THIS MUST BE THE WORST DAY OF MY LIFE!

And —
DON'T WORRY, NEV — IT'LL ALL SEEM BETTER IN THE MORNING.
IT HAD BETTER!
Next morning —
COCK-A-DOODLE-DOO!
SHRIEK!
YOU WERE WRONG, MUM. IT'S EVEN WORSE IN THE MORNING!
STOP COMPLAINING — THE SCHOOL BUS'LL BE HERE SOON.

Sure enough!
MORNING, YOUNG NEV!
GOOD GRIEF! MAYOR HADDOCK AGAIN!
BUS STOP
HAVE A NICE DAY, DEAR!
GIDDY-UP, BUS!
HERE'S THE SCHOOL.
SCHOOL
STOP RIGHT THERE, LAD — SAFETY FIRST!
STOP
Nev's story continues later in the book!

The Windy Island Illuminations.

Sun bathers on Windy Island Beach.

Water skiing on Windy Island.

Windy Islander in national dress.

Cuddles' Doodles
ME'S DRAWN 'OO, BRUVVER. LIKE ALLA PICTURES ME DID?

OO'S A ROTTER! ME'LL GET ME'S OWN BACK LATER!

WILBUR
The Wizard Twankies
ELVIS
TA-DA! ANOTHER TOP TRICK FROM THE WIZARD TWANKIES.
THAT'S US — THE BEST WIZARDS IN THE BUSINESS.
THE WIZARD TWANKIES TRAVELLING THEATRE SHOW
YEAH. BUT WHO'S THE BEST WIZARD OUT OF YOU TWO?
ER, UM . . .
WELL, SORT OF, WELL . . .
. . . WE'RE AS GOOD AS EACH OTHER.
. . . EXACTLY THE SAME. WE'RE CHUMS, PALS, BUDS, AMIGOS . . .

HEAR YE, HEAR YE. BECAUSE TELLY HASN'T BEEN INVENTED YET, HEAR YE! THE KING HATH A BAD CASE OF YE HICCUPS AND REQUIRETH A CURE.
WILBUR THIS SOUNDS LIKE A JOB FOR US.
IT DOES, ELVIS, MY SHORT MATE.
WE'LL DO IT!
YUS!
AND YE KING WILL PAY BIG BUCKS FOR THE CURE.
BIG BUCKS? MONEY?
SLAM
SEE YA!
DOOF!
WIZZ

HAR-HAR! THAT CASH IS GONNA BE ALL MINE!
OOH! MY POOR BEAK! YOU DID THAT ON PURPOSE, ROTTER.
PIFFLE! IT WAS AN ACCIDENT.
A...CHOO!
SHRIEK!
ZAP!
FZR
THAT WAS AN "ACCIDENT" AS WELL.
HIC
HAEC
HAK
HOC
WOOFYAH!
WIZARDS! AT LAST!

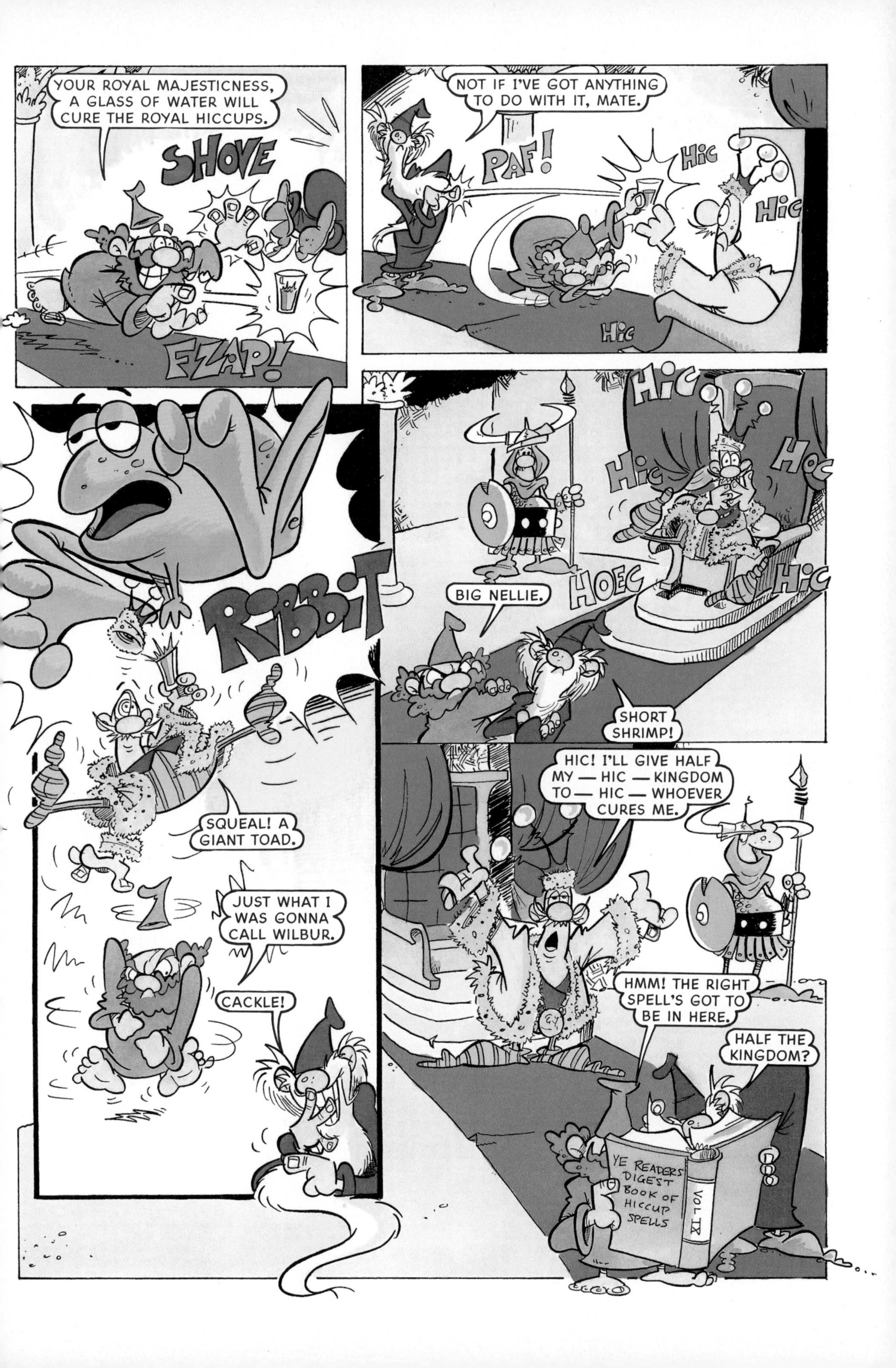
YOUR ROYAL MAJESTICNESS, A GLASS OF WATER WILL CURE THE ROYAL HICCUPS.
SHOVE
FZAP!
NOT IF I'VE GOT ANYTHING TO DO WITH IT, MATE.
PAF!
Hic
Hic
Hic
RIBBIT
SQUEAL! A GIANT TOAD.
JUST WHAT I WAS GONNA CALL WILBUR.
CACKLE!
Hic
Hic
HOC
HOEC
Hic
BIG NELLIE.
SHORT SHRIMP!
HIC! I'LL GIVE HALF MY — HIC — KINGDOM TO — HIC — WHOEVER CURES ME.
HMM! THE RIGHT SPELL'S GOT TO BE IN HERE.
HALF THE KINGDOM?
YE READERS DIGEST BOOK OF HICCUP SPELLS
VOL IX

I'VE HAD AN IDEA.
WELL, THERE'S A FIRST TIME FOR EVERYTHING.
HOO-HOO-HAR!
GOOD TO SEE YOU CAN STILL LAUGH AT YOURSELF.
FOOF!
OR AT MY SELF! YOU RAT-FINK!
YOU'VE NEVER LOOKED BETTER!
RIGHT! THAT JUST BLINKIN', BLOOMIN', FLIPPIN' DOES IT! NO MORE MR NICE WIZARD.
KOP FOR THIS, BEANPOLE.
DEFLECTAZITZ!
IN YOUR DREAMS, SHORT-STOP!
KA-ZITZ

?!?
ER, WOOPSY?
EEK! THERE'S A RAT IN THE ROYAL ROBES!
LOOK WHAT YOU DID!
ME? IT'S YOUR FLIPPIN' FAULT, NINCOMPOOP!
ZIPZ
HAVE SOME OF THAT! AND A BIT OF THIS AN' ALL!
SKITZ
ONLY IF YOU KOP A LOAD OF THIS!
ZAP
EEOUCH!
WOOH! OOOOH! ONE IN NOT AMUSED!
SQUEAK! I'M OFFSKI!

HEY, MY HICCUPS ARE GONE.
NATURALLY.
BET I CURED HIM.
IT'S JUST A PITY YOU HAD TO WRECK MY LOVELY CASTLE TO DO IT.
YOU DID THAT.
KNICKERS. IT'S YOUR FAULT.
DON'T WORRY. I'LL ZAP YOU A NEW CASTLE.
AND I'LL DO A BETTER ONE.
ZAP
MINE ARE BEST. GREAT RAMPARTS.
PIFFLE! I'M BETTER THAN YOU! MY TURRETS AND DRAWBRIDGE ARE THE BEST IN THE COUNTRY.
FZZ
OKAY, SO WHO'S GOING TO CURE ME OF THESE NITWITS?

BLINKY
L

BAH! THERE'S NEVER A BUS WHEN YOU NEED ONE.
PARP!
TOOT!
HONK!
PARP!
HOOT!
74
TOWN
READ THE DANDY
BUS STOP
ARE YOU GETTING ON OR WHAT?
AND I NEED TO GET DOWN TOWN TO THE SHOPS. OOPS! SHOULDN'T HAVE HAD BEANS FOR BREKKIE.

I'LL FLAG DOWN A TAXI.
TAXI!!
HEY! I'M THE CLOWN!
BLART!
GET LOST!

WET CITY! WHERE DID THAT DOWNPOUR COME FROM?
HA! HA!
OFFROAD PRACTICE AREA
DRIVE CAREFULLY!
DRIVING SCHOOL
AHA! A FLEET OF TAXIS!
THIS ONE LOOKS FREE.
DOZE!

AHA! NEXT CUSTOMER. DRIVE ON.
BRILLIANT CITY! IT MUST BE SELF-DRIVE!
SCREECH!
YEEHOO AND YEEHOO AGAIN!
Backwards charge! →

CLONK!
CLATTER!
DRIVE
AARGH!
IT'S A DAWDLE!
EEK!
DONK!
WAA!
SWERVE
WHIZZ!!
HOW AM I DOING?
SUPERB. HOW ABOUT ATTEMPTING TO GO IN **REVERSE** THIS TIME?

OKAY DOKEY! UP THE REVS . . .
VRUMMM-
-RRR-RRRUM!!

VAROOM!
. . . AND WATCH ME GO, AMIGO!!

BLINKY BEHIND THE WHEEL ALERT! RUNAWAY!
VROOOM!!
L
L
L
NEVER MIND RUNAWAY . . . FLEE YOUR PANTS OFF!!
!

L
WHUMP!

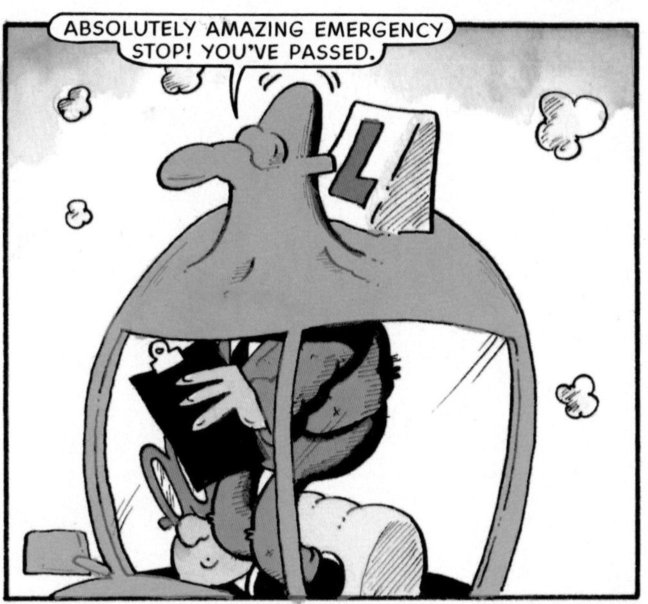
ABSOLUTELY AMAZING EMERGENCY STOP! YOU'VE PASSED.
L

THUD!
AND I'VE PASSED OUT!
PASSED, EH? MIGHT AS WELL GO HOME IF WE'VE PASSED THE SHOPS.

BONK!
DONK!
LESSON WRECKER!
CARAMBA! WHERE ARE ALL THESE HEAVY SHOWERS COMING FROM?

CREATURE FEATURES

BANANAMAN
in—
AS TIME GOES BY!
WHEN little Eric eats a banana, he becomes the Dandy's greatest hero, BANANAMAN!

One morning —
OH-OH! THAT'S THE CHIEF OF POLICE CALLING.

HELLO, CHIEF O'REILLY. IS THERE SOMETHING WRONG?
YES! I'VE GOT VERY PRESSING BUSINESS FOR BANANAMAN.

MUST BE SOMETHING SERIOUS. I'D BETTER EAT A 'NANA AND TURN INTO . . .

BOOM!
. . . BANANAMAN! BIGGEST, BEST, MOST HANDSOME, BRAINIEST HERO IN THE DANDY. AND ALSO . . .

. . . OUCH! A RIGHT PAIN IN THE BOTTOM.
GET MOVING. O'REILLY WANTS YOU NOW!
Editor's boot.

Soon —
SORRY ABOUT THE WALL, CHIEF. WHAT'S ON YOUR MIND?
NOT MY MIND — MY BACK! THIS GREAT BIG METAL THING! GET IF OFF ME.

Soon —
YOU'RE FREE NOW. WHERE'D THIS COME FROM?
IT JUST FLEW THROUGH THE BACK WALL.

Suddenly —
HEY! IT'S OPENING. LET'S TAKE A LOOK INSIDE.

But then —
YIKES! IT'S SUCKING US IN. HELP!
EEK!

LEGGO!
OW!

Then —
HA-HA! THEY'RE LOCKED IN MY TIME MACHINE. THEY'LL BE THERE FOR AGES AND AGES!

THAT'S GOT RID OF THEM. NOW, I, THE TIME TERROR, WILL BE ABLE TO RULE THE WORLD — AND OTHER THINGS.
OOH! I DON'T LIKE THE SOUND OF THAT.

THOSE TWO WILL BE STUCK IN THE PAST FOR EVER.

Chiefy and Bananaman are having a hard time going back through the centuries.
OUCH! TIME TRAVEL HURTS!
OH, SHUT UP! THIS IS NO TIME TO PANIC, BANANAMAN.

Soon—
WHUMP!
OOF! I THINK WE'VE LANDED.

WHERE ARE WE?
I HAVEN'T THE FOGGIEST.

Then—
EEK! A DINOSAUR WANTS US FOR DIN-DINS!
OO-ER!
ROAR!

MAYBE A BANANA SKIN WILL PUT THE SKIDS UNDER IT.
BAH! YOUR JOKES ARE OLDER THAN THAT MONSTER.

Suddenly—
OOF!
WHEE! IT WORKED!

MAYBE IF YOU ATE A BANANA, IT WOULD GIVE YOU THE BRAINS TO FIGURE A WAY OUT OF THIS.
THIS IS NO TIME FOR EATING —OR BEING CHEEKY!
Then—
OOYAH! I HATE IT WHEN FOOD COMES BACK ON ME!
YOU SHOULD HAVE KEPT YOUR EYES PEELED. TEE-HEE!
HEY! I'VE GOT A VERY GOOD IDEA.
YOU DO? WOW!
I DON'T KNOW WHAT HE'S UP TO, BUT HE'S KNOCKING EIGHT BELLS OUT OF THAT TIME MACHINE.
CRASH!
CLUNG! BANG!
And—
THERE! WHAT D'YOU THINK?
I THINK YOU'RE NUTS. HOW IS A METAL BANANA GOING TO HELP?

IT'S NOT A BANANA. IT'S A BOOMERANG! AND BOOMERANGS ALWAYS COME BACK. JUST WATCH!

And—
YAHOO! WE HAVE LIFT-OFF. — AND WE'RE TRAVELLING FORWARD THROUGH TIME!

WE'RE BACK HOME — SAFE AND SOUND.
CRUMP!
OOFYAH! GET OFF MY BACK!

HO-HO! NOW THAT ROTTER IS GOING TO DO TIME
HO-HO!
BAH!
TIME LOCK
HEE-HEE!

Cuddles
and
Dimples
CHEESY GRIN
CUTESY SMILE
FROWN
ME'S BEST.
GLOWER
NAW! ME'S BESTEST.

BLEURGH.
SEE? ME PULLED A FUNNIEST FACE.
POO, OO DID! ME'S BETTER AT MAKIN' FACES.
OKAY! OO PROVE IT.
UH?
NOO-O! 'AT'S FREEZIN'.
HEY! 'ATSA GOOD FACE!

YOU'S TURNS NOW — 'AVE SOME DRY RUSK CRUMBS DOWNNA NAPPY.
UH?
RUSKS
HO-HO!
OOH! 'AT'S ITCHYPOOS.
RIGHT! 'OO CAN HAVE 'IS LOT, CHUCKLES.
ME'S NAME IS DIMPLES, NOT CHUCKLES.
BIG BOX OF BUGS
FLING!
AN' 'EM'S LOTSA BUGS.

HELLO, BOYS. WHAT'S ALL THIS NOISE ABOUT?
NYAAAH! MISSED!
ARGH!
DIDN'T MISS DADDUMS.
YOU LITTLE PERISHERS! LOOK AT THIS PLACE. I'LL MARMALISE YOU BOTH!
OKAY. DADDUMS WINS!
HE'S PULLIN' A FUNNIEST FACE NOW.

THE TALE OF LOFTY McGRUBBER
This is the tall tale of Lofty McGrubber, Who was, even at birth, taller than his father and mother.
TALC
Though the child was so large, both parents were happy, Till the time came to change his oversized nappy.
And though they'd push and shove, heave and cram, They couldn't get Lofty to fit in a pram.
SHOVE!
STUFF!
Soon enough young Lofty was heading to school, Where all the kids laughed and made him feel like a fool.
HA!
HA! HA!
HA! HA!
HA! HA! HO!
Ho!
Ho!
Ho!
HA! HA!
SCH

All because on his first day
poor Lofty was late,
After getting his head stuck in
the top of the gate.

But soon they thought it great
that Lofty was tall,
When he helped the school win the
cup at basketball.

But the bad news was Lofty just
couldn't stop growing,
Soon his head stuck through the roof
— and it started snowing.

In half an hour Lofty was
covered in the stuff,
So he stormed off home,
deep in the huff.

When Mum saw him she yelled,
"What's wrong?" very loud.
But it was no good — his
head was now in a cloud.
LOFTY'S DOOR
Lofty was growing at an
incredible pace,
And soon his head stuck
out clear into space.
Lofty kept growing
— up and up he did shoot,
Until he could only stand
on Earth with one foot.
Till he was so large he toppled
— into space he was hurled.
Now Lofty's the tallest boy
not in the world.

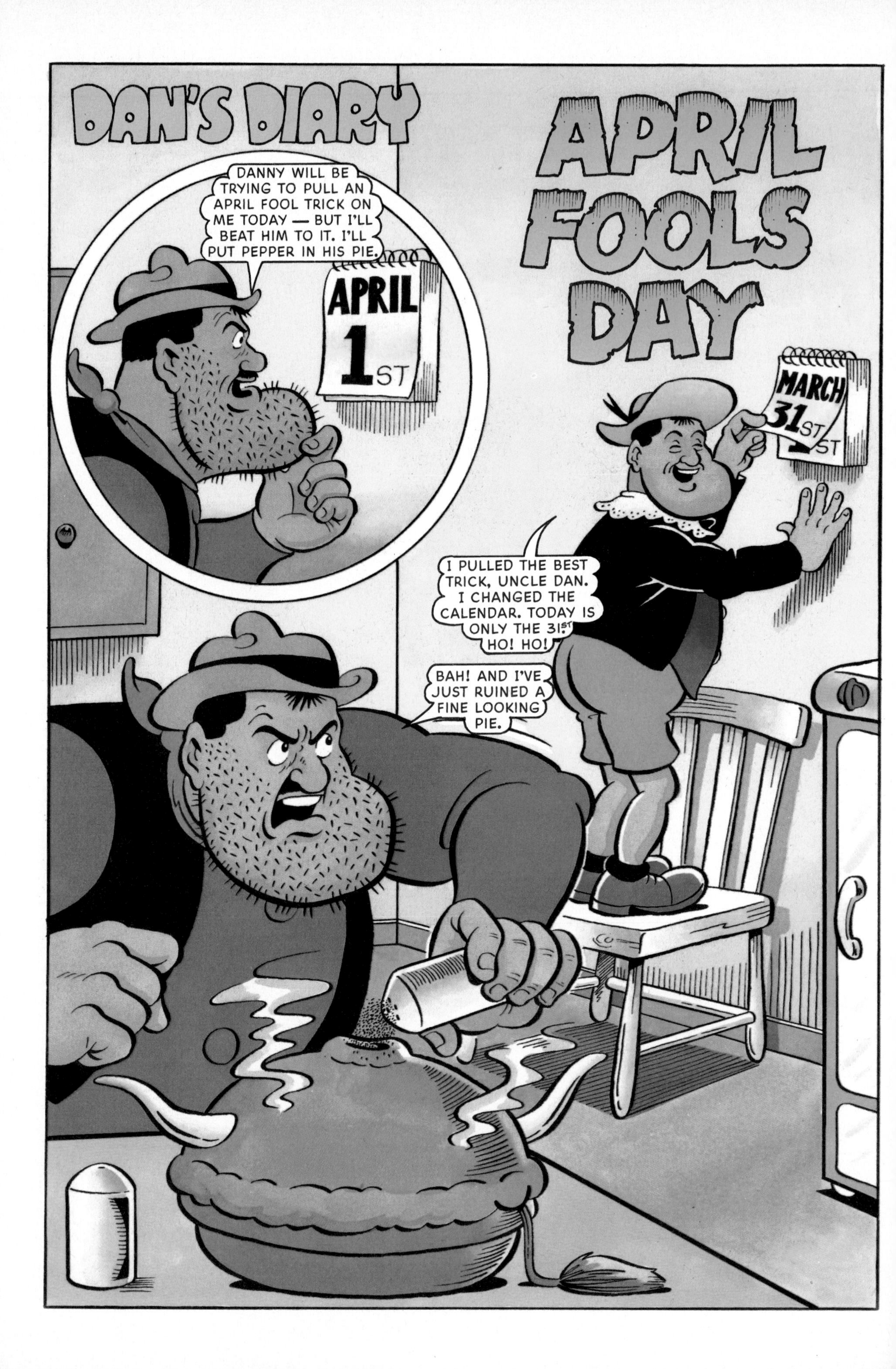
DAN'S DIARY
APRIL FOOLS DAY
DANNY WILL BE TRYING TO PULL AN APRIL FOOL TRICK ON ME TODAY — BUT I'LL BEAT HIM TO IT. I'LL PUT PEPPER IN HIS PIE.
APRIL 1ST
MARCH 31ST
I PULLED THE BEST TRICK, UNCLE DAN. I CHANGED THE CALENDAR. TODAY IS ONLY THE 31ST HO! HO!
BAH! AND I'VE JUST RUINED A FINE LOOKING PIE.

THE DANDY
WRECKING CREW
MUMMY!
HEY!
THE ONE THAT GOT AWAY WAS THIS BIG.
SAY CHEESE.
ROT! DON'T GET FISH THAT BIG!
GREAT CATCH!
PIRANHA
HEAVE!
FISH 'N' CHIPS
HA-HA!
EN GARDE!
OOYAH!
OI!
SOMETHING FISHY ALWAYS HAPPENS WHEN THE WRECKING CREW IS AROUND.
GLUP!
LIVE BAIT
SHRIEK! ME NOSE! ME BOTTY! ME EVERYTHING!

Welcome back to our Neville's Island story!
YOU ARE A MAJOR LOON — THERE ISN'T A CAR ANYWHERE ON THIS ISLAND!
STOP
Then —
INDEED NOT, YOUNG FELLOW . . .
. . . BUT THERE ARE SOME DEMENTED SHEEP!
GROAN!
SCHOOL
STOP

STOP
SCHOOL
COME IN! COME IN! NEVILLE — I'M YOUR TEACHER, MISS TWINSETT!
WHEN DO THE REST OF THE CLASS GET HERE?
WE'RE THE ONLY KIDS ON THE ISLAND!
I'M BIG ANGUS!

THIS IS MY SISTER, MORAG!
RASP!
I'M GINGER!
AND THIS IS MY TWIN BROTHER, CURLY!
IDENTICAL TWINS I SEE!
N
THIS IS KIRSTY.
D
C

But —
HUBBA! HUBBA! ER . . . HELLO!
YOU SMELL OF SHEEP!
RIGHT! LET'S START WITH A TEST.
SHOULD BE A CINCH AGAINST THESE COUNTRY BUMPKINS!
THE LIFE CYCLE OF THE BEETROOT? EASY-PEASY!
A DAWDLE!
LET'S SEE HOW YOU GOT ON.
Shortly —
OH, DEAR, NEVILLE — BOTTOM OF THE CLASS!
HO-HO! HE CAN DO A GOOD IMPRESSION OF A BEETROOT THOUGH!
0/10

RIGHT, CLASS — DINNER TIME!
COMING, MRS WILSON!
In the dinner hall —
SEAWEED AND GOATS' MILK IS THE BEST THING ON OFFER!
YEAH! YOU'LL EAT ANYTHING!
ROTTEN LOT!
After school —
GETTING THE BUS, NEV?
I'M NOT GOING ANYWHERE WITH YOU LOT!
Then —
SOUTH
UP
WEST
HERE
THERE
EVERY-
WHERE
NORTH
EAST
I DON'T BELIEVE THIS!
THIS IS THE WORST DAY OF MY LIFE! MUTTER . . . SCHOOL ON A HORSE . . . PSYCHOTIC SHEEP . . . SEAWEED FOR LUNCH . . . RIDICULOUS SHORT CUT . . . MUTTER!

CAN I HAVE THE SEAWEED AND GOATS' MILK, PLEASE?
IF YOU LIKE.
HO-HO! YOU CITY KIDS ARE DISGUSTING!
OVER THAT HILL IS THE QUICKEST WAY FOR YOU TO GET HOME!
After a while —
SOME SHORTCUT THIS IS TURNING OUT TO BE — PUFF!
I'LL ASK IN HERE FOR DIRECTIONS.
NO DOUBT SOME OTHER LOONEY WILL LIVE HERE!
But —
SURPRISE!
GASP! KIRSTY!

WOW!
WELCOME TO THE ISLAND, NEV!
THIS PARTY'S FOR YOU, PAL!
POP
I THINK I'M GOING TO LIKE IT HERE AFTER ALL!

KEYHOLE KATE
YOU'RE OBSESSED WITH KEYHOLES, KATE.
Simon Sandshoe — sporty type.
WHY NOT TRY SOME SPORTS?
IT'LL BE BORING!
SPORTS
BADMINTON'S NOT BORING . . .
. . . LOOK AT THAT KEYHOLE SHAPE!
And —
I'M WINNING AT CHESS.
GREAT KEYHOLE SHAPES!
I'M A WHIZZ AT PING PONG.
CLICK
CLICKETTY
CLICKETTY
CLICK
CLICK
CLICK
LOOK AT MY BAT!
I LOVE SPORTS NOW, SIMON!
WHAT A GIRL!

Dimples' Doodles
ME'S TURN, NOW. GOOD, EH?

RUBBISH! ME'D RATHER 'AVE NAPPY-RASH THAN 'OO FOR A BRUVVER.

Fiddle O' Diddle
I'M PREPARED FOR ALL TYPES OF WEATHER.
'CRASH HELMET' IN CASE OF HAILSTONES.
ANVIL TO HOLD HIM DOWN IN TORNADOES.
RUBBER Y-FRONTS IN CASE OF LIGHTNING
MULDOON IS THE BIGGEST IDIOT IN ALL IRELAND.
ANVILS 'R' US.
JOB OFFER! ONLY INTELLIGENT, ABLE PEOPLE NEED APPLY... AND MULDOON!
LOOK, MULDOON — THERE'S A JOB FOR YOUR OWN SELF.
Two minutes later —
YOU'RE HIRED, MULDOON. PAYMENT IS ALL THE BRICKS YE CAN EAT.
AMAZIN'! I NEVER EVEN OPENED ME MOUTH.
BOSS
AN EMPLOYER
FIDDLE IN DISGUISE!
THE JOB IS PAINTING A WHITE LINE DOWN THE MIDDLE OF THE CANAL.
DIDDLE-IDDLE! 'TIS RARE GOOD FUN WHEN MULDOON IS AROUND.
DER WHOITE PAINT

YOOPS!
HE'S TRIPPED OVER A FISH.
I'VE SWALLOWED SOME WATER AND GOT HICCUPS. HIC . . . HIC . . .
I KNOW SOME GOOD CURES FOR HICCUPS, SO I DO.
FIRST TRY HANGING UPSIDE DOWN IN A BUCKET OF CURRIED KIPPERS.
HIC! IT'S NOT WORKING. HIC!
REEKIN' HOT KIPPER VINDALOO
PAINTIN' YER HOOTER BLUE, HOPPING ON ONE LEG AND SINGING OPERA USUALLY WORKS, SO IT DOES.
BLOO
HA! HA! HA!
TRY PLAYING THE SAXOPHONE OUTSIDE MRS MACILPHATRICK'S HOUSE — REALLY LOUD.
HONK! BLAART!
TOOT!
PAARPLE!
WAKE MY BABY AND YE'RE DEAD.
RUSK

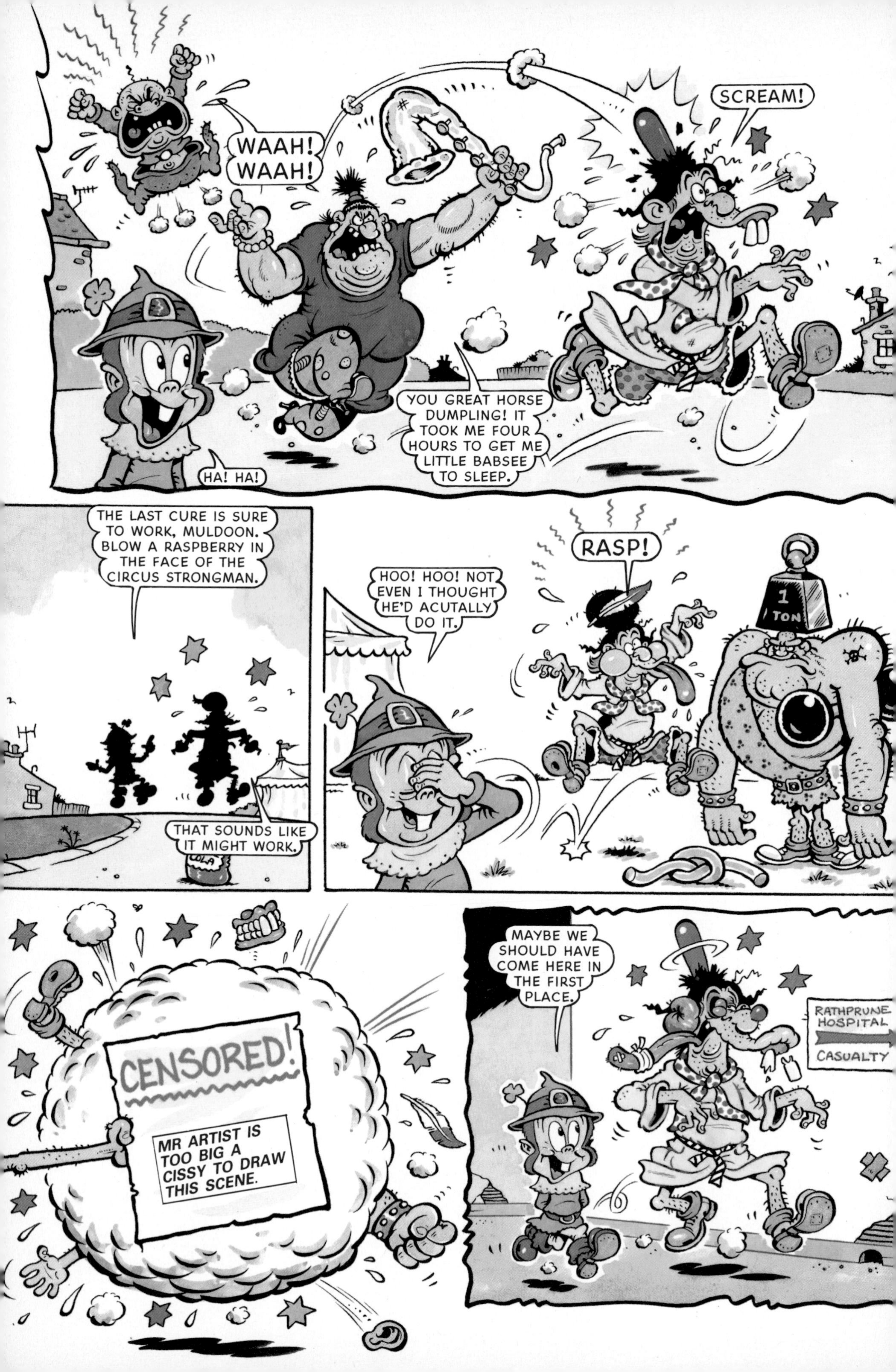
WAAH! WAAH!
SCREAM!
YOU GREAT HORSE DUMPLING! IT TOOK ME FOUR HOURS TO GET ME LITTLE BABSEE TO SLEEP.
HA! HA!
THE LAST CURE IS SURE TO WORK, MULDOON. BLOW A RASPBERRY IN THE FACE OF THE CIRCUS STRONGMAN.
THAT SOUNDS LIKE IT MIGHT WORK.
COLA
HOO! HOO! NOT EVEN I THOUGHT HE'D ACUTALLY DO IT.
RASP!
1 TON
CENSORED!
MR ARTIST IS TOO BIG A CISSY TO DRAW THIS SCENE.
MAYBE WE SHOULD HAVE COME HERE IN THE FIRST PLACE.
RATHPRUNE HOSPITAL
CASUALTY

CHEER UP, MULDOON. YE'RE HICCUPS ARE GONE . . . HIC!
RATHPRUNE HOSPITAL FOR THE BADLY BASHED.
AFTER COMMOTION LOTION
World of Tatties
ALL THE LAUGHING HAS GIVEN ME HICCUPS. HIC . . .
. . . HIC!
RIGHT — LET'S GET TO WORK ON SOME CURES.
COME TO DOCTOR MULDOON!
TIS A GOOD JOB FOR ME THIS CRAZY TALE IS ENDING.

HAW-HAW! SO THAT'S WHAT YOU MEANT.